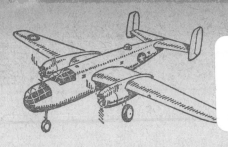

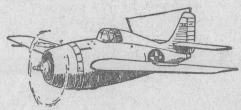

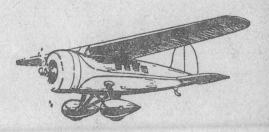

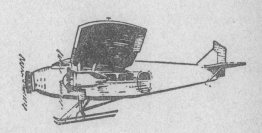

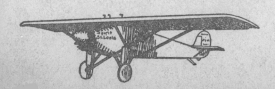

THEY FLEW TO FAME

by Robert Sidney Bowen

illustrated by Geoffrey Biggs
and Nel Clairmonte

WHITMAN PUBLISHING COMPANY
RACINE, WISCONSIN

CONTENTS

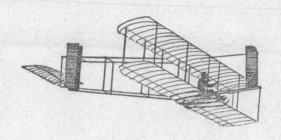

The Great Beginning
Wilbur and Orville Wright

The sun was a half hour above the eastern horizon the morning of December 17, 1903, when Carson Trent stepped out of his fisherman's cottage on the edge of the little seashore village of Kitty Hawk, North Carolina. All during the night a cold wind had blown steadily down from the north, and the pools of water left by the driving rainstorms of the past two weeks were frozen over. Out over the Atlantic there were moving rows of foamy white, and Trent scowled as he stared at them. There would be no fishing today in that icy wind and frothing sea.

With a shake of his head he went back into the cottage and into the kitchen where his wife was preparing breakfast, and his ten-year-old son, John, was dressing by the stove.

"It is too cold and blowy to go out in the boat today," he said, sitting down at the breakfast table, "so I might as well finish laying the floor in the new shed."

"Will you be needing me?" John asked quickly.

Trent looked at his son with raised brows.

"Of course I will," he said. "You know how to drive a nail, so why do you ask?"

"I thought maybe I could go over to Kill Devil Hill," the boy said after a moment's hesitation, "and watch those two men with their flying machine. Can I go just for a little while? I'll—"

Carson Trent stopped the rest with a scowl

and a vigorous shake of his head.

"You will stay here and help me," he said sharply. "A man fly in the air like a bird? That's rubbish! You keep away from those two fellows. They're as crazy as all get out. No telling the trouble you might get into."

"I don't think the boy would come to any harm, Carson," his wife spoke up gently. "I don't think those two are really crazy. They're just a couple of harmless cranks. That's all the folks are saying about them. Just a couple of—"

"I say they are crazy!" Trent shouted and pounded a fist on the table. "A pair of lunatics, thinking they can fly in the air like one of God's birds."

He paused to look at his son and level a gnarled finger.

"God didn't intend man to fly," he said sternly. "If He had He would have given him a set of wings. Now come eat your breakfast and say no more about those two."

"Yes, sir," John murmured, and he came to the table.

Four miles away from Trent's cottage the two men he had declared crazy stood on the sandy stretch of land by Kill Devil Hill shivering in the icy wind and casting apprehensive eyes up at the cloud-swept sky. One, the taller, was Wilbur Wright, and the other, who was slightly heavier, was his younger brother Orville.

For ten long years the two brothers had cherished the idea of one day flying a power airplane through the air. In those ten years they had made a thousand tests with kites and gliders they designed and built together. The previous fall they had come to Kitty Hawk from their home in Dayton, Ohio, and had made over a thousand test flights with their latest design, a biplane glider. And now they were back again with another biplane glider that was fitted with a four-cylinder, in-line gasoline engine of some sixteen horse-

power that operated two chain-driven propellers.

Three days before, on Monday the fourteenth, weather conditions had been ideal for an attempt to fly the powered airplane. A monorail track some sixty feet long, made of four planks laid on edge and topped with a strip of metal, was laid out on a level stretch of ground close by the crude shack they had built to live in. At one end of the track and facing into the wind, they set the machine with its sledlike skids on a board placed across a small block of wood to which had been fitted two bicycle wheel hubs. The rolling hubs were set one in front of the other, and they rested on the monorail track.

Both men had long been aware of what the people around Kitty Hawk thought of them, but what others thought did not bother them in the slightest. They were two men dedicated to a great dream and they were determined to bring about the fulfillment of that dream regardless of what others thought or said of them.

They had no desire or intention of fulfilling their dream in secret, however, and then telling the rest of the world of what they had done. They wanted witnesses present when they mastered powered flight. So they told the members of the Kill Devil Lifesaving Station, located not far away, that they would hang out a signal on their crude shack when they were about to make their first attempt at powered flight. The signal could be easily seen by the lifesaving station

men, and they would come over to witness whatever took place.

The signal had been hung out last Monday and
five men had come from the lifesaving station. To
decide who would attempt the first powered flight
the Wright brothers tossed a coin. Wilbur won.

Eventually all was ready for the attempt.
Wilbur took his flying position lying down on
the middle of the bottom wing, a little to the
left of the small four-cylinder engine that was
attached to the middle section of the bottom wing.
He started up the engine and while it warmed up
he held onto one end of a restraining rope that prevented the machine from moving forward until
he was ready. His brother stood holding the right
lower wing tip so that he could help maintain the
machine's balance as it moved forward along the
monorail track.

Finally the engine was warmed up enough and
Wilbur let go of the restraining rope. The machine
moved forward along the monorail track, but in

the matter of a few seconds the first attempt at powered flight ended in failure.

After a run of some forty feet the machine did lift itself a few feet into the air, but it suddenly turned sharply to stall and lose its flying speed and come down heavily on the left lower wing. When it hit the ground one of the skids dug into the sand and was snapped off. The damage to the machine was not great, but it had taken the Wright brothers two days to repair the damage and make the machine ready for a second attempt.

Now, on the morning of the seventeenth of December, the machine was ready, but there was the question of whether the weather was safe enough to make the second attempt.

It was biting cold, but far more important, the wind was blowing at about twenty-seven miles an hour. There had been hardly any wind at all when Wilbur had made his unsuccessful attempt, and perhaps the almost total lack of wind had been part of the reason for the failure. But was a twenty-seven-mile-an-hour wind too much wind? Would it perhaps blow the frail machine off the monorail track and severely damage it? Was a four-cylinder engine powerful enough to drive the machine forward in the face of a twenty-seven-mile-an-hour wind?

These and other questions were pondered silently by the two Wright brothers as they considered the weather conditions. Eventually Orville broke the silence.

"What do you think, Will?" he asked.

The older of the two brothers frowned and didn't say anything for a moment or two.

"I don't like this wind," he said presently. "Perhaps, though, it will slacken off some by the time we get everything ready."

"I have a feeling it will," Orville said. "It's less strong, I think, than it was when we woke up. And as the sun gets higher I think it will ease off. Enough to try it, anyway."

Wilbur smiled and made a gesture with one

hand toward his brother.

"Whatever you say," he said. "It's your turn, and if you want to try it, all right."

The younger Wright peered at the sky again, and nodded. "Let's start setting things up, and then we'll see," he said.

So the signal was hung on the side of the shack and in a short while four men and a boy came walking over from the lifesaving station. They were J. T. Daniels, W. S. Dough, and A. D. Etheridge, who were members of the station. The other man was W.C. Brinkley, of Manteo, and the boy was Johnny Moore, from Nags Head. Both happened to be at the lifesaving station when the signal was hung out, so they came along.

The three lifesaving station men had come over on Monday when Wilbur made his unsuccessful try, and they probably expected much the same outcome this time.

"Are you really going to try it in this wind?"

one of them asked bluntly.

"We think it will die down some by the time we are ready," Orville told him. "Anyway, we hope so."

"Maybe it will," the man said with a shrug. "Do you want us to lend a hand again?"

"If you will, please," Wilbur Wright said. "Help us lay out the track and set the machine on it."

"Glad to," the man said. "Let's get at it, then."

A few moments later they all began a task which on a warm day wouldn't have been much labor, but in the icy wind blowing down from the north, it proved to be torture. Several times as they laid out the monorail track they were forced to stop and go inside the Wrights' shack to warm themselves at a stove made out of a large carbide can. Later, while they were hauling the flying machine over and setting it in place on the track, they were forced again to retreat into the shack and warm their wind-chilled bodies.

During one of these trips J. T. Daniels asked

a question. "What do you call this machine? Do you have some special kind of a name for it?"

"Yes, we have a name for it," Wilbur told him. "We call it the *Wright Flyer.*"

"*Wright Flyer,* eh?" Daniels mused. Then with a smile and a shrug, he said, "Well, I hope for your sakes it does fly."

"It will," Wilbur said quietly.

"Yes, we feel certain of that," Orville agreed with a confident smile.

For a few moments there was silence in the shack. Then Wilbur looked at his watch and saw that it was just about ten o'clock. He held his hands to the stove once more and nodded at the others.

"Shall we finish the job?"

By half past ten the task of preparing for the attempt was completed. The *Wright Flyer* was in position for takeoff, and a camera was set up so that one of the lifesaving station men could snap a picture if Orville's attempt was a success. But when the Wright brothers once more measured the velocity of the wind with their hand anemometer they found that it was still blowing at twenty-seven miles an hour.

Should the attempt be made, or should they wait for a more favorable wind?

"I'll try it," Orville finally answered the unspoken question.

At a signal from Orville those who had come to witness the attempt moved well out of the way, except for the man who would take a picture of the flight if it were successful. He went to his position at the set-up camera, and Orville went over to the machine and took his lying-down flying position on the middle part of the lower wing. Wilbur took hold of the lower right wing tip to keep the machine in level balance, just as his brother had done for him on Monday.

Presently Orville started the engine and let it run to warm up while he held tightly to the restraining rope. As he listened to the throb of the engine he hoped and prayed with all his heart that this would be the day. The day after ten long years of trial and error, of hopes that turned into failures, and then new hopes that slowly turned into minor successes one by one.

He believed with all his being that man could make powered flight. He had complete faith in himself and in his brother. They had left nothing to chance. They had calculated and tested, and then calculated and tested again. Ten long years of testing, one faltering step at a time, like a baby learning to walk. High hopes one day, and then shattered hopes the next, but more new hopes again the day after that. This was the pattern through ten long years of a great dream.

He brushed aside the parade of rambling thoughts and looked over at his brother. Wilbur smiled and gave a little confident nod of his head. Orville smiled back and then turned his attention forward. There ahead of him was the metal-strip-capped monorail track, beyond the end of its sixty-foot length the stretch of flat sandy ground, and above all the air through which he and Wilbur had so long dreamed of making powered flight.

Was this to be the day?

He looked at his watch and the hands were at exactly twenty-five minutes before eleven. By now the four-cylinder engine was well warmed up and roaring its sixteen-horsepower song. Taking a deep breath, he let go of the restraining rope and concentrated every bit of his attention on the machine as it started moving forward.

It was moving, but very, very slowly, at a speed he judged to be only seven or eight miles an hour. The twenty-seven-mile-an-hour wind was proving to be too much for the struggling four-cylinder engine! He took a quick look at Wilbur holding the right lower wing and saw that his brother was having no trouble at all keeping pace with the slowly moving plane.

His heart sank, and the bitter taste of failure

was in his mouth, when suddenly the machine picked up speed. It moved faster and faster along the monorail track, and when he took another quick look at Wilbur he saw that his brother was running very hard in an attempt to keep pace and help balance the plane. A moment later, when the machine was still almost twenty feet from the end of the monorail track, Wilbur was forced to release the wing and duck aside.

Hardly had Wilbur let go of the wing when the *Wright Flyer* seemed to quiver from wing tip to wing tip, and then at the touch of Orville's hands on the controls it lifted clear of the monorail track and climbed up into the air to a height of ten feet. It had hardly reached the ten-foot altitude when it started to dart down toward earth again.

Furiously working the controls, Orville caught it in time and guided it back up to a ten-foot altitude. Once again it started earthward, however, and once more Orville caught it before it could touch the ground. Five times the machine started

to dive back down to the ground, but each time Orville managed to keep it in the air. It was a crazy, erratic, up-and-down flight because of the tricky air currents just off the ground, and because of Orville's complete lack of experience in operating a powered machine in flight. But it *was* powered flight—the first in the history of the world.

However, the flight was of short duration. At the end of twelve seconds the machine went darting earthward for the sixth time and Orville could not get it back up again. The machine sank down onto the sandy ground and went sliding forward on its skids to a full stop.

As Orville got down from the middle section of the lower wing, Wilbur came running over to him, his lean face beaming with the great joy of accomplishment they now shared together.

"You did it!" he shouted happily.

Orville smiled, but shook his head.

"No, Will," he said quietly. *"We* did it. Now

let's figure out the flight performance data."

As the four other men, and Johnny Moore, gathered around, they carefully measured the flight distance and found it to be 120 feet. Everybody agreed that the altitude had been ten feet, give or take a few inches. Wilbur had timed the flight with a stopwatch. It showed twelve seconds, exactly. That meant that Orville had flown the 120 feet at an air speed of thirty-one miles an hour.

Perhaps other men would have wanted to call it a day and celebrate the final achievement of their goal, but Wilbur and Orville Wright had no such thought. Achieving the fulfillment of their ten-year-long dream was but another beginning for them.

With the help of the four men and the boy they hauled the *Wright Flyer* back up to takeoff position on the monorail track. This time Wilbur flew it for a measured distance of 195 feet. After that Orville took a second try, and this time he flew the machine for a little over two hundred feet.

At exactly twelve o'clock noon Wilbur made his second flight. It was the best and the last of that greatest day in aviation history. He flew the *Wright Flyer* for the amazing distance of 852 feet and was in the air for a period of fifty-nine seconds.

That was the last flight of the day because shortly after it was made, as Wilbur and Orville were standing by the machine discussing the flight, a sudden violent gust of air blew the machine over on a wing tip and sent it tumbling across the sandy ground. One of the lifesaving station men, who was standing nearby, let out a yell and made a desperate lunge for the machine. The Wright brothers whirled around but, although they got their hands on the machine, it was too late. The wind wrenched it away from them and tumbled it over and over before leaving a broken and twisted mass of wreckage on the sand. One look at the crumpled machine and the Wright brothers knew

that their powered flights for 1903 had come to
an end.

They stood staring sadly at the smashed-up
flying machine, but the sadness did not in any
way lessen the joy in their hearts at having reached
their great goal. They had designed and built a
machine that could carry a man, lift itself off the
ground by its own power, fly forward without
losing speed, and come down safely on ground
that was as high as the ground from which it had

taken off into the air. They had proved that man can fly.

After lunch that day the two Wright brothers went over to the Kitty Hawk Government Weather Station to send a telegram to their father in Dayton, telling him the news and requesting him to release it to the world from Dayton. They had long ago decided that if and when their great dream did come true they would have the news released to the rest of the world from their hometown.

However, their wish was not to be granted.

As there was no commercial telegraph in Kitty Hawk their message had to be sent over the Government Weather Station wire to another Government Weather Station in Norfolk, Virginia. There it would be phoned to a commercial telegraph station in that city which would then relay the message along to Dayton.

The message was received by the Norfolk weather station operator, and he phoned it to the commercial telegraph office, but not until *after* he had told the news to a reporter who happened to be in the weather station at the time. That reporter quickly wrote up a story for his paper, the *Norfolk Virginia-Pilot*, but a story which when printed in the next edition was ninety-nine percent wrong. The reporter also offered his story to twenty-one newspapers throughout the country, but only five ordered it from him—and only two of those five printed the story.

So, not the Wright brothers' father but three newspapers first told the story to the world, and all three had the facts almost entirely wrong. Only one thing in their stories was correct. Each of the three stories did say that Orville and Wilbur Wright had flown a powered airplane through the air and landed it safely December 17, 1903.

Across the Channel
Louis Bleriot

Marcel Donnet drove the little Renault car along the poplar-lined road until he came to a fork. Stopping the car, he got out and walked forward to peer up at the road signs. Sun and rain had done much to obliterate the lettering, but he could still read it. The sign pointing along the right fork said LE MANS, and the sign pointing along the left fork said ORLEANS.

The **V** formed by the forking roads was a large field that was smooth and flat from one end to the other. A week before the field had been a small sea of undulating hay, but the hay had been cut and it was now a smooth yellow and green carpet soaking up the French July sun in the year 1909.

With a faint nod of satisfaction Donnet returned to the car and drove it up onto the edge of the field on the Orleans fork side. Braking it to a stop, he shut off the engine and made himself comfortable. He unbuttoned the collar of his shirt, took out a cigarette, and lighted it. As he drew the smoke into his lungs he tilted his head and blew it out again toward the sun-flooded blue sky.

"Life is good to you, Marcel Donnet," he murmured with a little smile. "You are a lucky man to be chosen by Louis Bleriot to be his mechanic. You are indeed!"

At that moment the creaking sound of cart

wheels came to his ears and turning his head he saw a little, ageless-looking farmer driving a wagonload of hay. He nodded his head in greeting and the farmer pulled his horse to a halt.

"You are in trouble, *monsieur?*" the farmer asked.

"Oh, no," Donnet said with a happy laugh. "I am waiting for Bleriot. I am Marcel Donnet, his mechanic."

The farmer nodded, but his lean, leathery face was a blank.

"So you are waiting," he murmured. "It is nice to wait in this warm sun. But the one you speak of, Bleriot. Who is he?"

Donnet stared at him in stunned surprise.

"You've not heard of Bleriot?" he demanded. "Louis Bleriot? The greatest aviator in all France? Perhaps in all the world?"

The farmer gave a little apologetic smile, and a flip of the whip he held in his hand.

"I am sorry," he said. "I am just a farmer, and

I hear little of what goes on beyond my farm. An aviator, eh? I know of the word, *monsieur*, but I am not sure what it means."

"An aviator pilots an airplane," Donnet explained patiently. "He flies it through the air from one place to another place."

"Flies . . . like a bird?" the farmer gasped.

"But of course!" Donnet exclaimed. "Do you mean to tell me you have never seen an airplane?"

"No, I have never seen one," the farmer said a little sadly. Then, giving Donnet a shrewd look, "It is really true? There is such a machine that flies through the air with a man in it?"

"It is not only true," Donnet said, "but you will soon be able to see for yourself that it is true. In a very short time none other than Louis Bleriot, himself, will be landing his monoplane in this field right here. I am here because he has told me to be here and meet him with the car."

The farmer's eyes had grown large, and he seemed to have to work his thin lips awhile before words would come out from between them.

"A flying machine is soon to come down in *this* field?" he gasped.

"That is so," Donnet said and looked at his watch. "Bleriot is flying his monoplane here from Étampes. He said he would leave Étampes at ten o'clock, and it is now half after. So he should be here very soon and then you will see a flying machine in the air with your very own eyes."

"And perhaps land on my head?" the farmer cried, his eyes growing even larger. "No, thank you, *monsieur!* I should like to keep my head for the few years I have left."

"But—"

Donnet was cut off, for the farmer had whipped up his horse and was sending it off along the Orleans road. He watched it until it was out of sight and gave an exasperated shake of his head.

"Scared imbecile!" he growled and took another puff on his cigarette.

A few minutes later he looked at his watch

again and saw that the hands were at twenty minutes before eleven. Putting the watch back in his pocket, he leaned forward on the car seat and peered at the sun-washed sky to the north of the field. And as he peered, little worried thoughts started creeping into his head.

Was Bleriot all right? Was he still in the air and flying toward this field he had described and pointed out on the map? Was this the right field? Yes, he was sure of that, but where was Bleriot? It was time for him to arrive. Had he met with trouble? Perhaps crashed? No, that was a stupid thought! Louis Bleriot did not crash. But had he met with trouble and been forced to land some-place? It was a thirty-three-mile flight from Étampes to this field at the edge of Orleans—the longest flight Bleriot had yet tried. So, had. . .?

He forced the rest of the thoughts away with an angry shake of his head and tried to relax, but it was impossible. The nagging little worry thoughts came sliding back. But then, at sixteen

minutes before eleven, his keen ears heard the
distant throb of a flying-machine engine. And
almost at the same time his sharp eyes caught
sight of a little monoplane silhouetted against the
golden blue above the north end of the field.

With a wild shout of relief and joy he jumped
out of the car and ran out onto the field, waving
his two arms in happy greeting. Coming to a stop
finally, lest he run straight into the path of the
landing monoplane, he watched Bleriot guide it
slowly and smoothly earthward, presently to
touch the wheels to the ground and go trundling
forward a short distance to a full stop.

When Donnet reached the airplane Bleriot had
climbed down and was stretching his legs. The
mechanic threw both arms about him and gave
him a tremendous bear hug.

"A perfect landing after a perfect flight, eh?"
Donnet cried. "You are truly the greatest aviator
of them all!"

Louis Bleriot smiled and after disengaging

himself from the bear hug he gave the mechanic a pat on the arm.

"It was a very fine flight, Marcel," he said. "Not a bit of trouble all the way. The engine ran perfectly—thanks, of course, to you. You know, some day I must make this same flight with you as my passenger. This part of France is so beautiful from the air. You would be thrilled, as I was."

"I am thrilled right now!" Donnet exclaimed with a laugh. "I am thrilled by this great flight you have just made. Thirty-three miles in just forty-five minutes. That is marvelous! It must be close to a record."

Bleriot nodded absently, but didn't say anything. Presently he smiled broadly and clapped his hands together.

"Now for a thousand British pounds!" he exclaimed.

Donnet stared blankly. "A thousand British pounds?" he echoed vacantly. "I do not understand this."

"The *London Daily Mail* has raised its prize offer from five hundred pounds to a thousand," Bleriot told him. "I could do a lot with all that money. Perhaps even start an airplane manufacturing business of my own."

"Yes, yes, of course," Marcel Donnet said hastily. "But I still do not understand. A thousand British pounds for what?"

"Flying across the English Channel," Bleriot said. "Last year they offered five hundred pounds, but nobody even attempted it. So, this year they are offering a thousand pounds."

Donnet had stopped listening after the first sentence. All the blood drained from his face, and he stood staring at the aviator as though he couldn't possibly believe that he had heard him correctly.

"Fly across the English Channel?" he finally gasped. "That would be madness. The impossible. Surely you are joking!"

Bleriot gave a quick shake of his head and

undid the buttons of his flying jacket.

"No, I am not joking," he said quietly. "On the contrary, I am most serious. It is only a bit over twenty miles from Calais, France, to Dover, England. And have I not just made a nonstop flight of thirty-three miles without one bit of trouble? So, why should a flight of a little over twenty miles be so impossible?"

But Marcel Donnet was not to be shaken.

"You must be mad!" he cried. "No, you don't mean it. It is still a joke. You can't be serious!"

Bleriot's eyes darkened for an instant, and then a mocking smile touched his lips.

"You have lost faith in me?" he chided, and he touched a hand to the wing of his monoplane. "You have lost faith in my machine that I designed and built with my own two hands. You have, eh?"

"No a thousand times!" the mechanic cried. "You and the machine have nothing to do with it. Nothing at all!"

Bleriot looked at him, brows raised in puzzlement.

"Now it is I who does not understand," he said. "What are you worried about?"

"The English Channel, of course!" Donnet exclaimed. "It can be a terrible stretch of water—even for ships. If you were forced to land you would crash and drown. You would die!"

"But I do not intend to crash and drown," said Bleriot evenly. "I intend to fly all the way across and win that prize of a thousand British pounds."

The mechanic groaned, shook his head, and came almost to wringing his hands.

"It is still madness!" he cried. "Perhaps next year when you have built a bigger airplane with a more powerful engine. But not in this little thing. You would be mad to try it!"

Bleriot laughed and spread his hands, palms up.

"So, I am mad," he said. "But are not all pioneers a little mad? Of course they are, or they would not be pioneers. Now, stop worrying. There are many things we must first do, and—"

He cut himself off with a shake of his head.

"But later about that," he spoke again. "Right now I want you to watch the machine while I drive into Orleans and send some telegrams."

He gave the monoplane's wing an affectionate pat and smiled at Donnet.

"Guard it well," he said. "It has made a splendid flight and deserves your tenderest care. I will be back in an hour, or possibly less."

Donnet nodded glumly and stared after Bleriot out of worry-filled eyes as the French aviator strode toward the Renault.

Six days later, on the eighteenth of July to be exact, Louis Bleriot had a worried look in his eyes, too, but it was not over the flight he was planning, and the chances of what might happen to him. On the contrary, it was worry that he might not be the first man to attempt an airplane flight across the English Channel. Another aviator by the name of Hubert Latham had announced that he was going to make the attempt in an Antoinette monoplane.

He did make the attempt, and before Bleriot was ready. At twenty minutes after six on a Monday morning, the nineteenth of July, Latham took off from the village of Baraques, near Calais, and headed out over the choppy gray waters of the English Channel, but he was not destined to reach the British side. At a point eight miles out from the French coast his engine stopped running and he was forced to land on the choppy water.

Fortunately for him the Antoinette had a somewhat boatlike body, and the wings were very thick. As a result the flying machine was able to float on the water long enough for a French destroyer to race out and pick him up.

Latham's failure did not deter Louis Bleriot at all. He was still determined to make the attempt himself. He decided to use the field at the village of Baraques, too, and set up camp there to prepare for the flight. Marcel Donnet was still very much against it, but he had stopped voicing words of protest that fell on Bleriot's deaf ears. The two men worked day and night on the little monoplane, powered by a three-cylinder Anzani engine of twenty-five horsepower, and by the afternoon of the twenty-fourth everything that could be done to insure a successful flight had been done.

Now, as it was to be so many times down through aviation history, the moment of takeoff depended on the weather.

For the last two days roving storms had covered both England and the Continent. For those early-day flying machines to try to fly over land in that kind of weather would have been suicidal, not to mention trying to fly over the treacherous English Channel.

However, during the evening of the twenty-fourth the storm clouds on both sides of the Channel faded away, and it was predicted by

the weatherman that the next day, Sunday, would
be bright and sunny. Bleriot decided to take off as
soon as it was light on Sunday morning. He was
ready, his monoplane was ready, and two members of the French Aero Club had arrived at
Baraques to declare his flight official in the event
that he did land safely on British soil.

At twelve minutes after five that Sunday morning he opened up the Anzani engine wide and went
rolling over the table-flat Baraques field. In hardly

any time at all the little monoplane lifted into the air and went prop-churning on its way out over the English Channel. Behind him those who had come to witness the takeoff cheered, but Bleriot did not hear them. Nor would he have paid much attention had he heard them, because as he climbed higher into the sky he saw something that absorbed every bit of his attention—huge banks of clouds directly ahead on the horizon.

The banks of clouds seemed to go right down and rest on the choppy gray waters of the Channel. There had not been a cloud in the sky when he was on the ground before takeoff, but once he was high enough in the air they seemed to appear as though by magic.

Bleriot scowled at them a few moments, and then shrugged. The weatherman had said there would be only sun and no clouds, yet there they were, forming up to bar his way. But he would not turn back! He had taken off and he was going to keep going, with the hope that when the time came he would somehow be able to get by the looming gray-white barrier.

With the aid of an ordinary compass he carried in his pocket he set a westerly course toward the British side of the Channel. The monoplane he flew was the latest of several he had designed and built, and he sincerely believed it to be the best. It was the smallest, the fastest, and the lowest-powered airplane then flying in France. The wings were only twenty-five feet across, and the body only twenty-six feet long. It was also the cheapest airplane to build, so if he did win the thousand pounds offered by the *London Daily Mail* perhaps he would go into the flying-machine manufacturing business. He. . . .

The thought was not completed because his attention had been drawn back to the cloud banks. They were not more than a mile or so ahead of him now, but he was suddenly able to see something he had been unable to see before. The banks of clouds were not resting on the water.

As a matter of fact, they were a good thousand feet above his altitude, and only stray patches of clouds were down on the water.

Breathing a sigh of relief, he continued to hold the little monoplane on its westerly course. The French coast was out of sight behind him now, but he had yet to see any sign of the English coast. A look at his watch showed that he had been in the air for only a little more than twenty minutes. Another fifteen and he should be able to see the English coast.

He flew onward and presently the main banks of clouds were directly above him, and several patches of clouds were scattered about in front of him. By banking the monoplane to the left or right he skirted around the edges of most of them, and he even flew right through one or two very small patches of clouds. But as he started to fly through one that didn't look very big he suddenly realized it was a lot bigger than he had thought. Rather than waste time trying to bank out of it he kept on going, until a few seconds later when he came out into clear air and a check of his compass showed him that he was flying due south instead of west!

Somehow he had managed to turn a quarter-way-around in the big cloud, but that didn't alarm him. All he had to do was turn west again and he was still bound to hit the English coast sooner or later. Just how far he had veered off course in the cloud he didn't know, nor exactly what correction to make so that he would arrive at the spot near Dover where he had announced he would land, and where some of his English friends should be waiting to greet him.

However, that wasn't so terribly important now. The important thing was to reach the English coast and land safely. That would still win him the *London Daily Mail* prize of one thousand pounds. That he should land where he had said he would land was not one of the conditions.

Hunching a little over the controls, he headed

the little monoplane west again and glued his eyes on the horizon ahead. For several minutes the horizon was but a line where distant clouds met the water. But eventually the line formed by the clouds meeting the water seemed to widen and grow darker and darker. He closed his eyes tight for a moment and then opened them again. This time there was no mistaking that ever-widening and ever-darkening line. It had to be land, and it had to be the English side of the Channel.

Four minutes later he flew over the coast, and there was not the slightest doubt he had reached England. He could tell from the type of houses he saw, and their little fenced-in gardens, that it was England, but he did not see any sign of a big city that might be Dover. He did see several fields large enough to land in, however, and that was joy enough for him.

Selecting the largest field, one that was bordered by a road leading to a cluster of houses, he guided the monoplane toward it. Presently he

landed the little machine and rolled to a full
stop exactly forty minutes after he had taken off
from French shores. He had succeeded and the
one thousand pounds were now his.

As he climbed out of the monoplane's cockpit
and down onto the ground, a figure in the uniform
of an English constable came running across the
field toward him. When the man reached Bleriot's
side he introduced himself as Constable Stanford
and asked if he could be of service.

"I am Louis Bleriot," the French aviator told him. "I have just flown my monoplane across the Channel from France. Could you tell me how far I am from Dover?"

"Just a few miles, sir," the constable told him. "This is called Northfall Meadow, and it's not far from Dover Castle."

The constable paused to stare at the monoplane and then back at Bleriot.

"You've flown this thing from France, sir?" he asked a trifle incredulously. "That must have taken a bit of doing, I'd say!"

"No, it was quite an easy flight," Bleriot told him. "But I would like to send some telegrams. Is there an office near here? And, would you be kind enough to stand guard on my machine while I go send them?"

"Glad to, sir," Constable Stanford said and pointed at the road bordering the field. "Just three minutes along that road and you'll come to a post office. They have a telegraph there and will be pleased to take care of you, I'm sure."

Louis Bleriot thanked him and walked across the field to the bordering road. Constable Stanford stood guarding the monoplane, little realizing then that he was the only witness to the successful completion of what would go down in aviation history as one of the most famous pioneering flights.

The Cups of Death

Manfred von Richthofen

Setting his coffee cup on the table, Baron Manfred von Richthofen, commanding officer of *Jagdstaffel* No. 11 of the Imperial German Air Force, went over to a window of his quarters and peered out at the sky. It was morning, the twenty-first of April, 1918, and although the sky was overcast the sun was fast burning through to make it another fine spring day. The young flying officer, only three months from his twenty-sixth birthday, nodded in silent approval, and the pleasure he felt lighted up his boyish-looking eyes. It was going to be another good day to lead his famous Richthofen Flying Circus into the air and shoot down more enemy planes.

He glanced at the wind sock atop one of the hangars and a frown knitted his brows. There was only a small wind, but it was blowing out of the east and that was not good. If any of his pilots got into trouble over the enemy lines and were forced to limp back home, they would have more trouble against an east wind blowing in their faces. This time of year the wind was almost constantly from the west or the southwest, but today, for some reason, it was straight out of the east and that did not please him.

A moment later he shrugged aside the unpleasant fact and walked out of the room and into another that served as his private office. Many trophies of aerial warfare hung on the walls, and there were more of them on corner shelves. When he entered the room his eyes went straight to the big desk where, standing on its smooth surface in perfectly aligned rows, were seventy-eight trophy cups that meant more to him than everything else in the room put together.

They were small and rather plain looking. Each was two inches high, an inch across the top, and the outside was of finely polished sterling silver. The inside was of a dull gold finish, and each was inscribed with the name of an airplane and a date. He called them his Cups of Death, for each one represented an enemy airplane he had shot down in combat.

There were seventy-eight on the desk now, but there would soon be eighty. Just as soon as the jeweler in Berlin filled his order for two more to represent the two air victories he had scored only the day before.

He stood staring at them for several moments, his young face a picture of prideful triumph. Then

he laughed and gave a vigorous nod of his head.

"Eighty!" he cried aloud. "Now that is a good round number!"

As the echo of his voice died away there came a knock on the outside door. Not taking his eyes off the Cups of Death, he shouted for whoever it was to enter. The door opened and a lean, straw-haired youth came inside. He was Lt. Hans Joachim Wolff, another of the squadron's crack combat pilots and Von Richthofen's closest friend.

"Good morning, Manfred," Wolff greeted Von Richthofen as he closed the door behind him. When Von Richthofen did not turn, he chuckled. "Ah, counting them to make sure none have been stolen?"

Von Richthofen swung around laughing and clapped him on the shoulder.

"Who would dare?" he challenged. "But I was just thinking, Hans. Eighty is a good round number, wouldn't you say?"

A slightly startled look showed in the newcomer's eyes.

"Yes, it is," he said. "But not enough, I hope. One hundred would be even a better round number."

Von Richthofen grimaced and his face sobered.

"That, I am afraid," he said slowly, "is impossible for me."

The startled look returned to Wolff's eyes and remained.

"Impossible for you?" he gasped. "Manfred,

why? Or are you just feeling very low this morning?"

The leading German air ace grunted, but did not speak for a moment.

"There have been rumors, and I have checked them," he spoke again heavily. "They are true!" He stopped to grind one balled fist into the palm of his other hand. "The High Command has decided that I am too valuable to be allowed to remain at the fighting front. I am shortly to be relieved of combat flying and recalled to headquarters for staff duty."

"No!" Wolff cried, as if in acute pain.

Von Richthofen sighed and made a little helpless gesture with his hands.

"Yes, it is true," he said. "But you are to say nothing about it, Hans. The order has not yet come through, and so there is nothing official as of the moment. Say nothing to any of the others."

"But of course, Manfred," Wolff said absently.

There was silence in the room for a bit, and

then Von Richthofen brightened and clapped Wolff on the shoulder again. "But there is good news, too!" he exclaimed. "Very good news for us both."

The straw-haired pilot stared at him gloomily. "I can't think of any that would please me now," he grunted. "But what is it?"

"Our leave has come through!" Von Richthofen said happily. "It is to start on the twenty-fourth. Only three days from now. And the full time was granted. Four weeks!"

In spite of the depressing news Wolff had just heard, his face brightened, also. "That is wonderful!" he admitted. "I could do with four weeks away from this blasted war. I. . . ." He stopped and gave Von Richthofen a frightened look. "But will you be recalled to staff during our leave?" he asked.

"No, I am sure of that," the other said. "We will have our full leave, and I will return here for a few weeks at least. High Command is going to recall me, but not that soon."

He laughed and gave a movement of his hand as if brushing that subject aside. "Wait until I take you hunting in the Black Forest, Hans!" he cried. "I will show you the greatest sport of all, and in the most perfect spot for it. You will—"

At that moment the air outside was suddenly shattered by a band booming out a popular German war song.

"What the devil?" Von Richthofen shouted angrily above the loud music.

"That is in your honor," Wolff said, laughing. "In honor of your two victories yesterday. The Commandant of the Fortieth Infantry Regiment has sent his band over to salute you."

"Well, I appreciate the honor!" Von Richthofen shouted. "But I do not wish to become stone deaf. Come, let's get out of here before our eardrums snap!"

While the honoring band outside continued to boom away, Von Richthofen and Hans Wolff went out the back entrance of the leading German ace's quarters and walked rapidly over to the hangars at the edge of the flying field. They went straight to the hangar containing Von Richthofen's plane. The mechanics working on the engine stopped at his approach.

With a smile and a wave of his hand that told them to carry on working, he started walking slowly about the airplane, caressing it with loving eyes. It was a Fokker Triplane and powered with a 200-horsepower Mercedes engine. From wing tip to wing tip, and from propeller to rudder, it was painted a bright red. Many Allied airmen had met that all-red plane in war-torn skies and died.

When he had completed his inspection of the plane, Von Richthofen went outside the hangar and looked at the sky. The sun had finally broken through and there were only scattered patches of clouds. The wind was still out of the east, though, and making the wind sock stand out a little stiffer than before.

A little dog came running up to the great German ace, wagging its tail, and Von Richthofen leaned over and stroked its head. Hans Wolff looked sharply at the dog and then at Von Richthofen.

"Have you forgotten, Manfred?" he asked.

Von Richthofen looked up at him, eyes questioning.

"Forgotten what, Hans?"

"That it is bad luck to play with a dog before

a patrol," Wolff said. "Remember when Stebbins played with a dog just before he took off? And Kurtz, and—"

"Rubbish!" Von Richthofen snapped, straightening up from patting the dog. "Don't tell me you believe all those silly bad luck omens? They're ridiculous, Hans! It wasn't patting a dog before a patrol that stopped them from coming back. It was better shooting and flying by the enemy. Stop talking like a superstitious child!"

Wolff flushed but managed a smile and a shrug.

"Of course you're right, Manfred," he said easily. "I just feel jumpy, I guess. It's nothing."

Von Richthofen laughed and playfully punched him in the ribs, and returned to studying the sky. He looked at that part of the sky that was over Allied-held ground and absently wondered if he would get the chance to add to his eighty victories today.

"We'll fly a patrol at eleven o'clock, or a little after," he said suddenly, still studying the sky far to the west. "The wind's east, now, but it may change. I want somebody to keep an eye on that new pilot, Wiltz. He's very green, and if he has to limp home I want somebody with him."

"He's flying in my flight, so don't worry," Wolff said quietly. "I'll keep an eye on him."

Von Richthofen lowered his eyes to look at his close friend and smiled. "Of course you will," he said. "I just mentioned it because of this east wind. I. . . ." He suddenly laughed and shook his head. "No, Hans, I'm *not* being superstitious. Simply practical."

Wolff returned the smile but didn't say anything.

"Well, I've some blasted paper work to do," Von Richthofen said a moment or two later, "so I might as well get at it. Have all three flights ready for takeoff at eleven o'clock. I'll have decided then if we'll go."

Wolff nodded. Because others were nearby he saluted smartly as Von Richthofen turned on his heel and walked back toward his quarters.

Due to a few minor adjustments that had to be made on the planes, it was eleven thirty when *Jagdstaffel* No. 11 took off into the air. Standing by his own revving Fokker, Von Richthofen watched as the three groups of five planes each climbed up through the April air. When they were finally in formation position and slowly circling about the field he took off and climbed up to a thousand feet above the others. Then at a signal from him the three-flight patrol headed west, steadily climbing higher as they winged along.

From his command position above, Von Richthofen took a good long look at each of the fifteen planes below him. He had taught those fifteen pilots practically all they knew about fighting in the air and returning home to fight again tomorrow. He was a stickler for perfection, and he was no less hard on himself than on any member of his Flying Circus. He had drilled them and drilled them, setting the example himself, and he now commanded what was readily admitted by friend and foe alike to be the finest air fighting unit on either side of No Man's Land.

When he had finished his inspection he gave his attention to the skies ahead. There were plenty of clouds that caused him to give a faint nod of satisfaction. Clouds were fine to hide above until it was time to go wing screaming down for a kill. Clouds were also fine to duck into and hide when things became just a little too hot. Clouds were a fighting pilot's friend in more ways than one. He always liked a sky with clouds in it.

Smiling at the passing thought, he lowered his gaze to the ground that was now a good two miles below his wings. Just ahead he could see the German trenches and the British trenches, with the twisting brown ribbon of ground that was No Man's Land in between. And considerably farther to the west he could just make out the French city of Amiens.

Looking down at war on the ground always

gave him a tremendous thrill. In the very early days of the war he had fought on the ground as a second lieutenant in the First Regiment of Uhlans. His fighting then had been against Russian forces and he had had many memorable experiences, but nothing to compare with fighting in the air above the war on the ground. War in the air was what he enjoyed most, and he knew that a little of him would die when the official orders came from Supreme High Command.

The rest of the thought vanished as his constantly roving eyes suddenly caught sight of aerial action many thousands of feet below him. Four Fokkers from some other German squadron had caught two low-flying British observation planes and were closing in for the kill. But as he watched he saw that the two British planes were not quite as helpless as they had appeared to be at first look. Both planes were putting up a terrific standing-off battle as they edged closer and closer to the safety of their own lines.

Still watching, Von Richthofen became certain that the German pilots were not going to let their intended victims get away, but he could not help but admire the flying and fighting skill of the British airmen in the much slower and far less maneuverable observation planes. Although he was a dedicated killer in the air, he was always quick to respect courage and openly admire skill in others, be they friend or foe. And so, as he stared downward, he paid silent tribute to the gallant but doomed British airmen.

His tribute lasted but a few fleeting seconds. At the end of that time his eyes caught sight of something else going on in the sky. It was something that might quickly alter the picture of the one-sided dogfight going on below. Seven British Sopwith Camels came ripping down out of some clouds to the rescue of the harassed observation planes below.

"No, you don't!" Von Richthofen shouted, and he waggled his red wings in signal to his squadron flying along underneath him.

Seconds later he had stood his red Fokker on its nose and was careening downward like a runaway comet. As he hurtled down past his squadron they dropped their noses, too, and followed him. The Sopwith Camels had now reached the fight below and were blasting away with all guns. Von Richthofen saw one of the original attacking Fokkers roll over on its wing, burst into flames, and go plummeting downward. He also saw the two British observation planes break safely away and go scooting far back over their own lines.

The first casualty had followed the opening of the attack by a fraction of a second. In the next second the whole sky was filled with British and German planes whirling and darting about with streams of winking red and yellow spurting from their noses.

Too late to catch the escaping British observation planes, Von Richthofen hauled his red Fokker out of its screaming dive and kicked it around

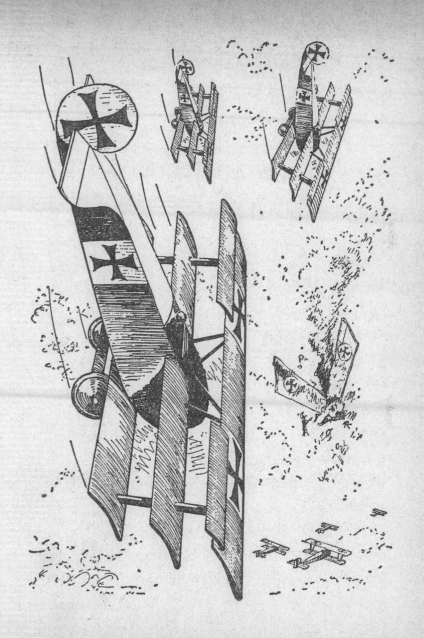

in a dime-turn to bring his guns to bear on a plane with British markings slicing by. But, before he could get around far enough to press the trigger trips on his joystick, the British plane had vanished, and in the air space it had occupied was a German Fokker slip-sliding downward with its whole tail shot off.

Banking even tighter to avoid the falling German plane, Von Richthofen cut away from it and out toward the fringe of the fight to select another victim and go in for the kill. That was the way to do it. Choose a target and dart in for the kill. No going around and around like a merry-go-round until you or the other pilot got the advantage of a tail shot. No, first pick your victim and then dive with blazing guns.

When he reached the fringe of the fight that seemed to spread all over the sky, he suddenly caught sight of a British Sopwith Camel some distance off. The plane was diving away from the air fight, as though its pilot had had enough and was retreating home. One look at the pilot who was making no effort to watch his tail and Von Richthofen knew that he must be a green pilot who had undoubtedly just received his first baptism of air warfare.

But, green pilot or experienced air fighting veteran, they were all the same to Von Richthofen, and he dropped his nose to dive down for the attack.

As a matter of record, the Sopwith Camel pilot *was* taking part in his first aerial battle. He was Lt. W. R. May, an Australian from Melbourne, and a member of R.A.F. Squadron 209. Before taking off with the others of his squadron, he had been instructed to stick close to the veteran pilots, to shoot down a German plane if he got the chance, but to light out for home if he got separated from his squadron mates. This was what May was doing when Von Richthofen spotted him and came thundering down.

Closing in fast on the Camel, Von Richthofen

snapped off a short twin burst from his guns and saw splinters fly off the center section struts of the other plane. Then, before he could lower his aim a hair, he saw the Camel pilot start to throw his plane all over the sky in a wild, frantic effort to shake off the attacking Fokker.

The wild maneuvering brought a laugh to Von Richthofen's lips. This was indeed going to be an easy kill—perhaps the easiest he had ever made. No matter what the Camel pilot did, Von

Richthofen knew that he couldn't miss. He was above and behind the other plane, and it had always been his proud boast that any enemy plane that got below and in front of him was doomed!

Perhaps the wild, crazy maneuvering by May in the Sopwith Camel amused Von Richthofen, and so he delayed sending a second shower of bullets from his twin Spandaus machine guns. Or perhaps he actually forgot for the moment about the big aerial dogfight going on above him. It will never be known because Manfred von Richthofen did not live to say.

Higher up in the sky another Squadron 209 pilot saw that Lieutenant May was just this side of certain death. He was Capt. Roy Brown, a Canadian with twelve downed German planes to his credit.

The instant he saw May in serious trouble he broke away from a Fokker he was engaging and went hurtling down in a desperate effort to reach May in time. In a matter of seconds he had dived a couple of thousand feet and was slamming in on Von Richthofen's tail. He opened fire and saw his bullets ripping into the tail of the Fokker Triplane. Nosing up a hair, he sent his bullets traveling up the fuselage.

When they reached the cockpit the all-red Fokker faltered in the air and slowly fell over on one wing. It hung there a moment and then seemed to right itself and go sliding down toward the middle of No Man's Land. Just above the ground it leveled off a little. The wheels touched and the plane went bumping forward over the uneven ground until one of its wheels came off and it half fell and half slid into a shell hole.

As May flew safely on toward home, and Captain Brown wheeled back up into the air fight that was still raging, an Australian infantryman dashed out from the British trenches to attach a rope to the tail of the red Fokker Triplane so that it could be hauled back to the British lines. He found Manfred von Richthofen sitting up straight in the cockpit, his hand gripping the joystick, stone dead!

On the afternoon of the day following his death, Baron Manfred von Richthofen was buried in Bertangles Cemetery with full British military honors. Six British Royal Flying Corps pilots acted as pallbearers, and a squad of Australian infantrymen fired a salute over the grave.

Prize of Battle
Eddie Rickenbacker

It was Sunday, October 27, 1918, and in another fifteen days World War I would be over. Nobody knew then that the eleventh of November would mark the end of the great conflict, but on the Allied side of the lines there was pretty good reason to believe that the end would not be long in coming.

Austria had collapsed, and there was a quite

obvious weakening in the strength of German forces from one end of the Front to the other. The enemy simply did not have sufficient reserves of troops, guns, tanks, airplanes, and other equipment of war. As one Allied soldier is said to have expressed it, "All the Boche has left is his bare hands."

So the end seemed near to the Allied forces, but the German High Command had not yet given up. It still hoped for a miracle that might alter the existing situation and gain desperately needed time . . . a miracle such as a surprise breakthrough in force that would split the Allied lines and create general confusion.

It was a hope, and a very thin one, but shortly before the twenty-seventh of October, plans were drawn up by the Germans, and put into operation, to entrain every possible German fighting unit that could be spared to the Grand Pré sector under the cover of darkness. There troops and equipment would be unloaded and sent to strategic

points in the German lines. Then, when everything was in place, a massive assault would be
made along the entire Front.

This mighty do-or-die effort by the Germans
was doomed from the start. Allied Intelligence
heard about it and Allied Air Reconnaissance
confirmed all rumors. It was even known by the
Allies that the enemy would make its "secret"
concentration of forces and equipment at Grand
Pré on the night of the twenty-sixth. Allied bombing squadrons were alerted to hammer that area
into dust, just as soon as it was light enough to
see the targets, on the morning of Sunday the
twenty-seventh.

It was also known, and to be expected, that
the Germans would put up all the air strength they
could spare to patrol the Grand Pré area and
protect the movements of their assault forces.
So the task of driving off the German fighter
planes and protecting the Allied bombers was assigned to certain Allied fighter squadrons.

One of those squadrons was the American Ninety-Fourth Pursuit Squadron. It was the famous Hat-in-the-Ring Squadron, commanded by Captain Eddie Rickenbacker, America's leading air ace.

The Ninety-Fourth flew French-made Spads, powered by 200-horsepower Hispano-Suiza engines, and it was the crack pursuit squadron of the American Air Service. It had produced eight air combat aces: Raoul Lufbery, Douglas Campbell, Redd Chambers, Hamilton Coolidge, Thorn Taylor, Jimmy Meissnor, Ward Cook, and the top American ace, Eddie Rickenbacker. The Ninety-Fourth had shot down more enemy planes than any other American squadron, and it had also flown more hours of combat patrol than any other of Uncle Sam's air fighting units.

As soon as it was light enough on the morning of the twenty-seventh, Rickenbacker led the Ninety-Fourth off the ground for its special patrol. And for a change the weather was fairly good.

For the last few days the weather had been so dirty there had hardly been any patrols flown, but the weather had changed overnight and Sunday dawned a mostly sunny day for flying, fighting, and possibly dying.

The bombers that the Ninety-Fourth and other pursuit squadrons were to protect were British-designed DH-9's powered by an American-designed and -manufactured Liberty engine. The Liberty Bomber, as it was called, had soon proved itself a failure as an efficient bombing aircraft. It was very slow and very clumsy in the air, and the faultily constructed gas tanks presented a perfect target for enemy incendiary bullets. The Liberty Bombers became known as the Flaming Coffins because of the many brave men who died in them.

When the Ninety-Fourth reached the Grand Pré sector, the air above it was already filled with planes—Liberty Bombers, American pursuit planes, and swarms of German single-seater fighter planes. A number of the planes showed the bright red noses of the famous Richthofen Flying Circus. The great German ace had met his death in the air months before, but the pilots he left behind had carried on and continued to make the Richthofen Circus the most feared of all German air fighting units.

The Circus now flew the Fokker D-VII, a plane that was equal to, if not better than, any pursuit plane the Allies were putting into the air. For

some time the Allied Air Command had longed to get its hands on a forced-down and captured Fokker D-VII so that it might be studied in detail. Thus far, though, every D-VII brought down either had been destroyed in the air, or its pilot had set fire to it on the ground before he was captured.

There were a number of these killers in the air over Grand Pré, slashing away at the lumbering Flaming Coffins and inflicting a terrible toll with their blazing Spandaus aerial machine guns. Even as Rickenbacker gave the signal for the Ninety-Fourth to dive to the attack, he saw three Liberty Bombers become balls of raging flame falling earthward.

A few moments later the pilots of the Ninety-Fourth Pursuit were in the middle of the meleé of twisting and turning and diving planes. The brave pilots and observers of the Liberty Bombers were giving the German troop and equipment concentrations below an unmerciful pounding, and even at that early hour it was obvious to those in the air that the secretly planned German offensive was going to be blown to bits before it even got started.

The air battle, however, continued to rage furiously. Perhaps the German fighter pilots realized full well that the battle on the ground was lost even before it got started, but that did not mean they had also lost the air battle—not yet, at least. They flew and fought like devils possessed. As a result, not all the airplanes hurtling down to destruction on the ground were the lumbering Liberty Bombers. There were American pursuit planes also falling in flames.

One of the American pursuit planes destroyed in the air did not meet its fate from the blazing guns of the Richthofen Flying Circus, or from any other guns of German planes. It was the victim of a direct hit by German antiaircraft fire, or ack-ack guns, as they were called. The pilot of the ill-fated Spad was Ham Coolidge, a close friend of

Eddie Rickenbacker's, and one of the best-liked and most popular pilots in the Ninety-Fourth Squadron. He was one of its top aces, and like most of the others he had flown through more barrages of antiaircraft fire than one could count on fifty pairs of hands.

In World War I antiaircraft fire was pretty much of a laugh to airmen. At least it was after they became seasoned to it. The rate of hits on a plane by antiaircraft fire was said to be one in seven thousand, and then only a hit caused by bursting shrapnel, never a direct hit by a shell that had not yet exploded.

What happened to Ham Coolidge was the exception. Gallant air fighter that he was, Coolidge had broken away from the main dogfight to go to the aid of some Liberty Bombers struggling to get back home. The big planes had dropped their bombs and were almost back across the lines when four Fokkers dropped down out of nowhere and started blasting them to pieces.

Coolidge was almost within range to open fire on the attacking Fokkers when his horrified squadron mates saw an antiaircraft shell score a direct hit on the nose of the Spad and blow both pilot and plane to smithereens. It had never happened before, and those who were watching actually doubted what they saw until notes were compared when they later returned to their airdrome, and they were forced to believe it.

A few moments after Ham Coolidge met his unusual death, Eddie Rickenbacker suddenly saw holes appearing in his left lower wing, and jerking his head around he saw a red-nosed Fokker sitting on his tail spitting lead at him out of both guns. Even before he saw the Fokker he was in action. The bullet holes in his left lower wing told him enough, and as he jerked his head around he was already hauling the Spad up the front side of a gigantic loop.

The Fokker pilot tried to follow him up by looping, too, but Rickenbacker gained greater height and half-rolled over to drop down on the German's tail. A short savage burst from the American ace's guns caught the Fokker right on target. It fell over on one wing, seemed to stagger for a short distance, and then went tumbling down to crash on the ground far below.

By then most of the Liberty Bombers were on their way home. The German pilots, at last finding themselves being outflown and outfought, were breaking off from the big air battle and heading eastward at full throttle.

Eddie Rickenbacker chased one of them well behind the German lines, hoping for a chance to score his second air victory of the day, but the fleeing Fokker had a head start and a speed equal to that of the Spad. Rickenbacker was unable to close the gap between them. He was also dangerously far behind the German line, so he finally gave up the chase and went cutting around and back toward the west.

As he neared the lines his alert eyes caught

sight of a two-plane air battle off to his right and a couple of thousand feet above his altitude. It was a lone Liberty Bomber struggling to get home, but not making very much progress because of a lone red-nosed Fokker D-VII harassing it with blistering, aerial machine-gun fire.

Opening up the Hispano-Suiza's throttle wide, Rickenbacker sent his Spad, wings screaming, up toward the obviously one-sided fight. True, the Liberty's pilot was making a desperate effort to shake off the attacking Fokker so that he could stagger home. The Liberty's observer was getting in some good bursts with his own guns that were forcing the German pilot to break out of his short diving attacks. But Rickenbacker could see that it was only a matter of time. The Liberty's engine had been hit and the propeller was hardly turning over. Any second now the engine might quit cold and the bomber become a perfect target gliding toward the Allied side of the lines. If that happened, the Liberty's pilot would have a choice:

Let the German shoot him down, or swing around to glide back and land on German-held ground and become a prisoner of war.

Fortunately the Liberty's pilot was not forced to make any choice. Rickenbacker had gained the height he needed and was closing in on the German Fokker with guns blazing. Undoubtedly the German didn't even know Rickenbacker was there until he heard the hammering of the American ace's guns. In a flash, though, he broke off his attack on the crippled Liberty and sent his plane up in a high-climbing loop.

Perhaps he thought that the Spad would rip by under him and he could roll off the top of his loop and come down on its tail. That maneuver was as old as aerial warfare and Rickenbacker wasn't fooled by it for an instant. He immediately pulled his Spad up in a loop, too, and came out on the top of it on a level with the Fokker and still in firing position behind it. Lining it up in his sights, he was just about to open fire when he saw something that halted the movement of his thumbs on the trigger trips.

The Fokker pilot had tried for too much altitude in his loop, and he had lost all speed before he could come out on the top of it. As a matter of fact, the Fokker's engine had stopped for some reason, and Rickenbacker could see the propeller motionless across the nose as the German plane literally hung by its nose in the air.

It was a sitting-duck shot for the American ace. He was so close he couldn't possibly have missed, but he did not fire. He couldn't.

It was not part of Rickenbacker's fighting code to cold-bloodedly kill a helpless and defenseless enemy. He never had in any of his aerial combats, and he couldn't do it now. In the days of World War I, aerial combat was, in a sense, a sport. True, the stakes were usually life for the winner and death for the loser, but there were certain unwritten rules of sportsmanlike conduct, and for Eddie Rickenbacker one of them was never to kill a helpless and defenseless foe.

So he did not fire on that Fokker D-VII hanging almost motionless in the air. At the same time he certainly had no intention of letting the German pilot fall out of his stall and go back eastward to land on German-held ground. He had plans for that Fokker. It was a D-VII and it would be a perfect prize of war if he could force the pilot to glide across the American side of the lines and force-land in a field where he could be captured by ground troops before he had time to set fire to his plane.

Even as he watched the Fokker begin to slide tailfirst and then roll over on its wing, he pictured taking it up for a joy-hop around the airdrome tomorrow before turning it over for careful inspection by Allied technical experts. It was a very pleasing thought he had, but he did not let the little daydream lull him off guard.

A moment or two later, when the Fokker was fully out of the stall and had twisted over, nose toward the ground, Rickenbacker cut his Spad in even closer. He fired a short burst across the Fokker's nose as its pilot started to swing around toward the east. That short warning burst was all that the German needed—at least for the moment. He instantly straightened out his plane and went gliding toward the American side of the lines.

The Fokker had originally stalled at a height of some ten thousand feet, and so Rickenbacker knew that he had plenty of altitude in which to get the German well behind the American lines where he could force-land in a field. True, it would be another air victory for him even if the German cracked up in some field pockmarked with shell holes, but that wouldn't get him a joy-hop in the German's plane tomorrow, or the Allied Air Command a Fokker D-VII to inspect.

Sitting a little behind and above the gliding Fokker, Rickenbacker herded it westward toward the American side of the lines. Three times the

German suddenly stuck his nose down for speed and tried to whip around and get back to German ground, but each time Rickenbacker was ready and waiting for the maneuver. A short burst zipping by the Fokker dangerously close changed the German's mind in a hurry each time and sent him swinging toward the west.

A fourth attempt did not come, for the simple reason that after the third failure both planes were so far behind the American lines, and so low, that German territory could no longer be reached in a glide.

It was only then that Rickenbacker took his eyes off the German plane for a few moments to peer ahead and down at the terrain below. At first he couldn't see a single open area big enough to serve as a landing field. Then a good-sized, fairly smooth field came into view—and what was even more pleasing, there were some Allied soldiers along side of it who would unquestionably race out and capture the German at rifle point before he could destroy his plane.

A short burst from his guns and some hand signals by Rickenbacker quickly told the Fokker pilot where he was to land. The German, apparently resigned to his fate, acknowledged the signals and promptly proceeded to do as ordered. Ever alert to any last-minute tricks, Rickenbacker maneuvered his plane to a position where he could streak down and open fire if the German acted as though he were going to deliberately crash his plane, or if the soldiers along the edge of the field were not fast enough in reaching the plane.

The German gave no sign, however, that he had any desire to risk his own neck by making a crash landing deliberately. He floated down another hundred feet or so toward the field and came around in a smooth, graceful, gliding turn that brought him over one end of the field and into the wind. Another hundred feet or so and he would be down on the ground. Out of the corner of his eyes Rickenbacker could see some of the

soldiers starting to run out onto the field with
their rifles at the ready position.

Then it happened!

From out of nowhere came another Spad. It
was in a power dive and headed straight for the
landing German Fokker with its guns blazing. Its
markings were very blurred and Rickenbacker
couldn't tell whether it was an American, French,
or British Spad. As a matter of fact, he never did
find out, but right then the nationality of the

Spad's pilot wasn't of the slightest importance. What was important was that the pilot was firing long-range bursts of aerial machine-gun bullets in an effort to shoot down the Fokker D-VII.

No sooner had the strange Spad appeared and opened fire than Rickenbacker dived on it and fired a long warning burst with his own guns. Whether the other Spad's pilot heard Rickenbacker's guns above the yammering of his own, or saw the American ace diving on him, is something else that will never be known. In any case, he ceased firing at the Fokker at once and went wing-screaming away to become lost to view in the distance.

But the damage had already been done.

In a frenzied effort to escape from the blazing guns the German pilot had turned his still-gliding plane sharply to the left. As a result, instead of being in a good position to land on the smooth field, he was now headed straight for another field, one that was full of shell holes and shattered tree trunks. He was far too low to glide-turn again and get back over the smooth, unobstructed field. He could only glide straight ahead to an inevitable crash landing.

From his position in the air Eddie Rickenbacker sadly watched as the Fokker hit the lip of a shell hole and bounced high into the air. It flipped over on its back and came down to hit the ground again and scatter wreckage in all directions.

By an odd twist of luck the German pilot was not seriously injured. He crawled out from under the mess of wreckage, got to his feet, and waved his hand in a gesture of thanks to Rickenbacker. Then he calmly turned around and walked with both hands in the air toward the running soldiers.

Eddie Rickenbacker waved and circled about until the soldiers had taken charge of their prisoner. Then he banked and flew off toward the Ninety-Fourth Pursuit Squadron's home airdrome, a very angry and disappointed man.

"Just Plain Suicide!"
Charles A. Lindbergh

George Bell walked slowly along the Pelham railroad station platform, waiting for the eight-seventeen that would take him into New York City and another day at the advertising agency. There was a hint of rain in the low-hanging cloud layer that May morning in 1927, but off to the east there were breaks through which the sun was beginning to show.

When he reached the end of the platform and was turning back he saw Frank Jones, a neighbor and friend of his, thumbing through the pages of the *New York Times*. He walked over and tapped him on the shoulder. "Mind if I read, too?" he asked pleasantly. "They were all out when I got to the stand."

Frank Jones swung around with a startled look that quickly changed to a smile. "Oh, morning, George," he said and proffered the paper. "Here, help yourself."

Bell chuckled and shook his head. "Just kidding, Frank," he said. "I'll pick up one in Grand Central. Is there anything world shattering?"

"Not world shattering," the other replied. "But another pilot has arrived at Curtiss Field, out on Long Island, to try the New York to Paris flight. He's going to try it alone."

Bell grimaced and made a little gesture with one hand. "Alone?" he echoed. "He must be crazy. Who is he? Somebody famous?"

"I've never heard of him before," Jones said with a shrug. "Young fellow, only twenty-five, by the name of Charles Lindbergh. He used to be an airmail pilot, and he's a captain in the Air National Guard. The *Times* has quite a story about him."

"Anything to fill a column," Bell said with a laugh. "But what does it say? That the kid should be quietly taken away before he kills himself?"

"No, nothing like that in the *Times*," Jones replied with a short laugh of his own. "But Lindbergh is quite sincere in his belief that he can do it. And he seems to have convinced some other people, too. A group of men in St. Louis are backing him and bought the plane he is going to fly. He calls it the *Spirit of St. Louis*. It's a cabin monoplane manufactured by the Ryan Aeronautical Corporation in California, and it was made especially for this flight. I guess he means business, all right."

"I still say he's crazy," Bell said. "How big

is his plane, anyway? Is it like Commander Byrd's three-engined Fokker, the *America?*"

"No, it's just a small, single-engined plane," Jones told him. "The engine is a Wright Whirlwind. Around two hundred horsepower, I think the *Times* said. But he did fly it nonstop from San Diego to St. Louis, and then from St. Louis to New York. That's pretty good."

"It's not New York to Paris," Bell said. "Over the Atlantic Ocean! I think I read somewhere that it's thirty-six hundred miles from New York to Paris."

"That's right," Frank Jones confirmed. "The thing I wonder about is how he is going to carry all the gas he'll certainly need on a flight that long. I imagine, though, he has that all figured out, or he wouldn't be making the attempt."

"If he really is, and it's not just some new-fangled publicity stunt," Bell said. "Something the airplane's manufacturers thought up to get a whole lot of free advertising. Frankly, I think this whole crazy business about flying nonstop from New York to Paris is just something to give aviation in this country a publicity boost."

"I wouldn't know, but I doubt that," Jones said with a little shake of his head. "Commander Byrd did fly over the North Pole, and I don't believe he'd lend his name to something that was just a shim-sham publicity thing. And don't forget, there have already been some test flight crashes by pilots who were going to try it, and three or four people were killed. That's pretty expensive publicity, if you ask me."

"Perhaps it isn't just for publicity," Bell said with a shrug. "Perhaps it's really on the level, and one of them will actually get there. I read where Commander Byrd is taking along two pilots— Bert Acosta and Bernt Balchen—to do the flying for him. At least that makes some sense. But for a kid like this Lindbergh to try it alone would be just plain suicide!"

"I'm inclined to agree with you," Frank Jones

said. "I'd say he's taking a very foolhardy risk just to win twenty-five thousand dollars. On the other hand, though, I imagine whoever does it will make several times that amount afterward."

"What's the twenty-five thousand about?" Bell asked. "Has somebody actually offered that kind of money?"

"A New Yorker by the name of Raymond Orteig," the other replied. "He made the offer some time ago. Twenty-five thousand dollars to the first man who flies nonstop from New York to Paris, or from Paris to New York. As a matter of fact, two Frenchmen have already tried it from Paris to New York."

"They have?" Bell exclaimed in surprise. "I hadn't heard anything about that. But I've been so busy lately I've hardly glanced at the papers. What happened? They didn't make it, of course?"

"Apparently not," Jones said and touched the newspaper he had tucked under his arm. "I was just reading a little piece about them. A Charles

Nungesser and an André Coli. Nungesser was a French air ace in the war. Anyway, they took off from Paris three days ago, but not a word has been heard of them since. They must have gone down in the Atlantic someplace."

"Two more," Bell murmured and shook his head. "Well, I hope that puts some sense in this Lindbergh. If two couldn't make it, what chance does he think he's got trying it alone?"

"None at all, as I see it," Jones commented. "He's the only one who's said he was going to try it alone, and I think somebody should stop him. Why, even that other fellow, Clarence Chamberlin, who plans to try it in the Bellanca monoplane, *Columbia,* isn't going to try it alone. He's taking somebody with him. Just who, it hasn't been announced yet, but there'll definitely be two of them in the plane."

"As you say, somebody should stop Lindbergh," Bell said emphatically. "He doesn't stand a chance. He'll only kill himself."

Frank Jones nodded but didn't say anything because at that moment the eight-seventeen came sliding into the station.

There were a great many people who shared the opinions of George Bell and Frank Jones in that month of May, 1927. And a number of them were directly connected with the American aviation industry. Much as they would like to see it done, they simply did not believe it was humanly possible for one man to fly nonstop from New York to Paris alone. No matter how fine a pilot he might be, the mental and physical strain of such a flight would be too much for one man. Lindbergh was bound to fall asleep at the controls and go plunging with his airplane down into the dark waters of the North Atlantic. The publisher of a leading aeronautical magazine was most emphatic in his assertion that Lindbergh would succumb to mental and physical fatigue and should therefore be prevented from taking off.

Out at Curtiss Field on Long Island, Charles

Lindbergh went quietly about his preparations for the flight, quite conscious of the storms of protest and criticism raging about him, but as confident as ever that he would succeed in reaching Paris. There were a number of preparations to keep him busy and his mind off what the vast majority of people were thinking and saying. There was the replacement or repair of various parts of the Wright Whirlwind engine and of the plane. There were cockpit instrument adjustments to be made, and the installing of a barograph by a member of the National Aeronautics Association to record time and altitude so the flight could be declared official in the event it was a success.

There was much to be done, but at least he didn't have to make all the preparations for the flight alone. No sooner had he arrived from St. Louis than he was offered the cooperation and assistance of people he had never met before. Shortly after his landing, the technical experts of the companies that manufactured the equipment of the *Spirit of St. Louis* came to Curtiss Field and offered their services in preparing for the flight.

Lindbergh was deeply grateful for all the expert technical help they gave him, but he was distressed by the horde of reporters and news photographers that dogged his every step. A few of the reporters showed him courtesy and respect, and when they wrote their stories they reported fact and not fiction. The majority, though, saw

in Lindbergh's venture only a chance to write headline stuff that would sell newspapers. The truth was not important. That Lindbergh's plan to fly nonstop from New York to Paris was actually a carefully planned scientific and technical aeronautical venture, and not something in the same class as flagpole-sitting, probably never even occurred to them. However, as preparations for the flight progressed, the hundreds of stories that were written, right or wrong, did catch the attention and the imagination of the entire country.

By Thursday morning, the nineteenth of May, all that could be done to prepare the Ryan monoplane for the flight had been accomplished. All that was needed now was word from the noted meteorologist, Dr. Kimball, of the New York City weather bureau, that the weather along the Great Circle Route from New York to Paris was suitable for the flight.

During the past few days the weather had not been good for the attempt, and on the morning of the nineteenth it was even worse. There was light rain from New York all the way up through Maine. There was heavy fog along the coasts of Nova Scotia and Newfoundland. Ships far out at sea reported that there were signs of a storm developing in the Atlantic west of France.

When the weather would get better no one could say with any degree of accuracy. It might be within hours, or a couple of days, or even a week. All Lindbergh could do was wait.

The young pilot had another worry that had nothing to do with the weather. As a matter of fact, he had two worries. One was Commander Byrd's Fokker, *America,* and the other was Clarence Chamberlin's Bellanca, *Columbia.*

That these aircraft had not already taken off on the attempt to fly nonstop to Paris was due in one case to an unfortunate accident, and in the other case to bickering among men. Tony Fokker, the designer and builder of the *America* had made a crash landing after a flight test of the craft, and several days were required to repair the plane and retest it for the flight. In the case of Chamberlin's *Columbia*, it had not been decided who would accompany him as second pilot and navigator. According to reports there was quite an argument in the *Columbia's* camp as to who that man should be.

By the nineteenth the *America* was all repaired and tested, and an official christening of the aircraft was scheduled for the twentieth. That over with, the *America* would be ready whenever the weather was. Although no word had yet come from the *Columbia's* camp about the second man, there was no reason to believe he wouldn't be picked in a hurry should the weather over the Great Circle Route suddenly become favorable.

During the day Lindbergh kept in touch with Dr. Kimball's office, but when the reports indicated that the bad weather was probably going to continue for a while, a couple of his friends made plans to take him to see a show, *Rio Rita*, that was playing in New York. As Lindbergh and his two friends were driving to the theatre, however, he decided to check once more with Dr. Kimball's office.

One of the men in the car, Dick Blythe, went into a drugstore and phoned the meteorologist. When he returned to the car he had news which was slightly encouraging. The weather was starting to clear, very slowly, over the Atlantic. Also, a storm reported to have been forming west of the French coast had apparently dissipated itself, and the weather there was changing from poor to fair.

While his two friends waited quietly, Lindbergh thought the situation over from every angle. This might be the break in the weather he had been waiting for, or it might be only a temporary improvement. Should he leave at once, or should he wait until tomorrow to see if the weather actually had continued to improve?

After several minutes of silent deliberation he

decided that he would drive out to Curtiss Field and begin the last-minute preparations. As Curtiss Field was not nearly long enough for him to risk taking off with fully loaded gas tanks, he had planned to fly the *Spirit of St. Louis* from Curtiss Field to Roosevelt Field, adjoining Curtiss. He would fill and top off his tanks there, then take off from the mile-long runway that Roosevelt offered. He would go straight to Curtiss Field now, make his preparations, and then get a couple of hours of sleep before flying over to Roosevelt Field when it was light. He would also make a last-minute check with Dr. Kimball's office on the weather. If the report was still encouraging he would go.

Because of one thing and another Lindbergh was able to catch only an hour's nap in the early morning of the twentieth. When he came out of the small hotel where he had rested, fine rain was falling from low-hanging clouds, and the air was much too hazy to risk flying the *Spirit of St. Louis* from Curtiss to Roosevelt even with a small

amount of gas in the tanks. The aircraft was hitched to a truck and was towed over to the head of the other airfield's mile-long runway.

By then it was three o'clock in the morning, but in spite of the hour there was quite a crowd of people standing around in the rain waiting to see what was going to happen. Word had quickly spread that Lindbergh was making last-minute preparations, and the reporters and the curious came swarming to Roosevelt Field. Most of them doubted that he would actually go—not with that rainy, cloud-ridden sky.

However, it was not the weather at Roosevelt Field that concerned Lindbergh the most. He had flown in considerably worse weather many times as an airmail pilot. His big concern was the weather he would encounter along the Great Circle Route. A final call to Dr. Kimball's office and he decided to go. The weather along the route was not good, but it was steadily improving. A heavy fog north of New York and all the way to Newfoundland was lifting, and there were no further reports of storms on the French side of the Atlantic.

The tanks in the *Spirit of St. Louis* were filled and topped off, but when that was done Lindbergh was suddenly confronted with an entirely new problem. A five-mile-an-hour east wind had swung around to the west. That meant that instead of taking off into the wind he would be taking off downwind. The runway was soggy with rain and there were several pools of water on its surface. There was still a haze under the low-hanging clouds, but, most dangerous, there was a string of telephone wires just beyond the far end of the runway. He would not only have to take off downwind in his heavily loaded plane, but he would have to get off the ground in time to gain sufficient height to clear those wires.

Standing beside the *Spirit of St. Louis*, with its engine idling, Lindbergh looked along the soggy runway and at the telephone wires beyond the far end. He looked at his plane, at the wheels sunk in the rain-mushed ground, and at some of the aeronautical experts who had helped him prepare for the flight and who were silently returning his glance.

It was now close to eight o'clock in the morning, Eastern Daylight Time. Presently Lindbergh nodded his head, turned around, climbed into the *Spirit of St. Louis*, and shut the cabin door behind him. He ran the engine to full revs and made a final check of the instruments. When he was satisfied, he nodded through the cabin window at the men waiting to pull the chocks away from in front of the wheels. When the chocks were clear he opened the Wright Whirlwind up wide.

It roared out its song of 220 horsepower, but the quivering *Spirit of St. Louis* seemed to barely crawl forward. Several men ran forward and started shoving on the wing struts in an effort to make the plane move faster. But the rubber-tired wheels, half sunk in the soft ground of the runway, seemed to fight all the efforts of the Wright Whirlwind to increase the speed. Some of the observers were sure the Whirlwind would tear itself apart before the plane had traveled fifty feet. Others were more convinced than ever that Lindbergh was a crazy fool about to get himself killed.

For some twenty or thirty feet the plane just barely moved along the soggy runway; then it began to pick up speed. The men pushing on the

struts had to let go and duck out of the way. The pace continued to increase, and presently the plane was moving fast enough for Lindbergh to get the tail up.

But the speed was still considerably under what was needed to lift five thousand pounds into the air. And with every revolution of the propeller there was more precious runway sliding by under the wings. Water splashed up from the pools as her wheels spun through them and the telephone wires drew ever closer. To everybody watching it was no longer a question of whether Lindbergh would fly to Paris, but rather, would he even get off the ground in time to clear the telephone wires.

Every pair of eyes was glued to the *Spirit of St. Louis* as it virtually staggered along the rain-soaked runway. They saw the plane lift clear of the ground but almost instantly sink back down again. It rose once more and again sank back. Then, when the telephone wires were less than a quarter of a mile away, the *Spirit of St. Louis* lifted into the air once more, and this time it did not sink.

The climb was agonizingly slow. The plane seemed to have to strain desperately to gain a foot of altitude, and then another one. Everyone held his breath and waited as the plane struggled for altitude. Finally a tremendous sigh of relief could be heard as the *Spirit of St. Louis* succeeded in clearing the wires by no more than twenty feet and went struggling on upward. When there were some two hundred feet of air under the wings, Lindbergh gently leveled off and banked around toward the northeast and onto the first leg of the Great Circle Route.

At six minutes before eight Charles Lindbergh was off the ground and on his way to Paris.

Beginning with that moment, the whole world started waiting and watching and listening. As Lindbergh flew up the New England coast toward Nova Scotia and Newfoundland, there were constant reports of his plane being seen. That night, when he was last reported from Newfoundland as having headed out over the Atlantic, millions and millions of Americans prayed for his safety.

Their prayers were answered. When dawn came, Lindbergh was still flying the *Spirit of St. Louis,* and he was right on course. However, the weather he had encountered during the dark night had been vastly different from that predicted. Nature had hurled every kind of hardship at him— rainstorms, snowstorms, and sleet. There were howling winds that made the clouds boil, and fog so thick it was like a solid wall being pushed along by the nose of the plane.

But in spite of all the bad weather thrown into his path, Lindbergh flew on, and finally he sighted land. He saw the southern tip of Ireland, and then the southern coast of England. A little later the coast of France came into sight just as the sun was sinking out of sight behind him in the west.

He flew onward, right on course, toward Paris. Darkness had closed down on him for the second time, but he found the city and the Le Bourget Airdrome. At twenty-two minutes after ten o'clock, Paris time, he landed in the middle of Le Bourget Airdrome and gently braked the *Spirit of St. Louis* to a full stop, after flying 3600 miles nonstop in thirty-three hours and thirty minutes!

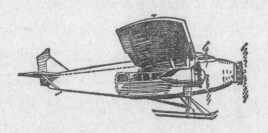

To the South Pole
Bernt Balchen

It was the night before Thanksgiving, November 28, 1929. In the camp of the Commander Byrd Expedition in Little America there was no bustle of preparation for a turkey feast on the morrow. Excitement centered elsewhere.

True, there would probably be something a little special in the way of food the next day for the men in the camp, but four of the expedition's number were not planning to be there for the holiday dinner. They were Commander Byrd, Captain Ashley McKinley, Harold June, and Bernt Balchen. Their plans for Thanksgiving were to make aviation history . . . the first flight by man over the South Pole.

Three years before, May 9, 1926, Commander Byrd, with Floyd Bennett as his pilot, had flown in a Fokker Trimotor monoplane from Spitsbergen over the North Pole and back. And tomorrow, Thanksgiving Day, 1929, an attempt would be made by Commander Byrd in a Ford Trimotor monoplane, named the *Floyd Bennett,* to fly from the Little America camp out over the South Pole and back.

For many months careful preparations had been made for this flight. The Ford Trimotor was dug out of its winter covering of frozen snow as soon as spring came to the Antarctic. It was minutely inspected from wing tip to wing tip, and from the propellers of the three powerful

Wright Cyclone engines clear aft to the tip of the tail. Then, with specially designed skis attached in place of the conventional wheel-type landing gear, the big airplane was test-flown again and again until it was in absolutely perfect shape for the dangerous flight over the South Pole.

Finally the plane was ready. Now the date of the flight depended on the weather.

Summer had come to the Antarctic, but that did not mean continuous days of fair winds and sunny skies. There was light both day and night, just as there is during the Arctic summer, but it was several hundred miles from the Little America camp to the region of the South Pole, and when there was fine flying weather at the camp there could also be death-trap weather over the Pole.

On the fourth of November a small expedition, headed by Dr. Larry Gould, had left the Little America camp by dog sled for a 450-mile journey of exploration to the base of the Queen Maud Mountains that stood between the Little America camp and the South Pole. In addition to exploration and surveying work, the Gould party would perform three other functions. It would set up a series of food and supply depots extending to the base of the Queen Maud Mountains. It would inform the Little America camp by radio of the weather conditions in the Queen Maud area. And it would serve as an emergency rescue party in the event the flight to the South Pole was terminated by a forced landing.

Another precaution taken to insure the success of the flight to the Pole and back had to do with the matter of fuel for the *Floyd Bennett*. As the aircraft could not carry enough gas to take it to the Pole and back, it was necessary to cache a supply of reserve fuel at the base of the Queen Maud Mountains so that the *Floyd Bennett* could land there on the return flight from the Pole and take aboard the gasoline needed for the last leg of the flight to the Little America camp. Not long after the Gould party had left camp, the reserve supply of gas was loaded aboard the *Floyd Bennett* and flown to a point at the base of the Queen Maud Mountains where it was unloaded and cached, and the location plainly marked.

From that point on south to the Pole would be the most dangerous part of the flight because the peaks of the Queen Maud mountains were higher than the heavily loaded Ford Trimotor would be able to reach. There were only two routes through the peaks at an altitude it was believed the aircraft could reach. One was by way of the Axel Heiberg Glacier, and the other by the way of the Liv Glacier. Whichever was chosen, the weather would have to be ideal if the plane was to make it.

On Thanksgiving eve Dr. Gould had radioed that the weather over the Queen Maud Mountains was good, and Commander Byrd made the decision to attempt the South Pole flight the next day. The decision to go was sweet music to the ears of Bernt Balchen, whom Commander Byrd had selected from the small group of pilots at the Little America camp to do the flying of the Ford Trimotor. He felt as if his cup of joy was finally being filled to the brim.

Bernt Balchen had been born in the small village of Tveit in Norway, October 23, 1899, and from earliest boyhood his one great ambition had been to fly an airplane. Most of all, he wanted to fly an airplane through polar skies.

He had learned to fly a plane and had progressed step by step toward the daring flights he dreamed of. When Commander Byrd was at Spitsbergen, Balchen gave him advice and help that went a long way toward making the North Pole flight the success it was. When Commander Byrd returned to the United States, he brought Bernt Balchen with him to be a member of the *America's* crew when that plane finally did fly the Atlantic nonstop a month or so after Lindbergh.

Balchen was aboard the *America* as co-pilot, but he did almost all of the flying because Bert

Acosta, the pilot, possessed very little experience in instrument flying, and the fog and clouds the *America* encountered were too much for him. Balchen took over the controls when they were not very far out over the Atlantic. It was Balchen who made a safe landing in the water near Ver-Sur-Mer on the coast of France when pea-soup fog closed in every available landing field, and the *America's* gas tanks went dry.

Because of his splendid piloting on that flight, and because of the many logbook hours Balchen had piled up flying in far northern skies, Commander Byrd had taken him along on the Little America Expedition.

Now, Balchen's greatest ambition was about to be realized . . . a polar flight that would make history. He was not to be the co-pilot, or a spare man going along, just in case. He was to be the pilot of the airplane!

Being a rather unassuming and taciturn man, Balchen kept the joy that he felt to himself and went right to work making a final check of the airplane. With the mechanics he went over the *Floyd Bennett* once more. When he was satisfied he ordered the five wing tanks and the fuselage tank filled. He had an additional supply of gasoline in five-gallon cans placed inside the plane.

Everything that was put aboard the airplane was carefully weighed so there would be no chance of overloading. At the last minute, though, Commander Byrd decided to take along two

150-pound bags of extra food, just in case of a forced landing on the ice. Balchen was not pleased at all with the extra weight, but Byrd was the leader of the flight and the one who made the decisions, so he didn't say anything about it.

Takeoff time drew close. It was nearly half past three on Thanksgiving afternoon, and the *Floyd Bennett* rested heavily on its ski landing gear as Balchen ran up the three engines for a final check. It remained only for the three other members of the flight crew to come aboard, and they did in the next minute or two. There were Commander Byrd, the leader and navigator; Harold June, the co-pilot and radioman; and Captain Ashley McKinley, the aerial photographer of the flight.

At exactly twenty-nine minutes after three, Balchen opened up all three engines. For an instant the big skis held fast to the packed snow. Then they let go and the Ford Trimotor moved forward. It picked up speed with a rush, and at the right moment Balchen lifted it from the snow and ice surface of Little America and climbed up through the polar air to an altitude of fifteen hundred feet. There he leveled off and set the plane on the course Commander Byrd had given him.

Man was on his way to the South Pole by air.

The weather over Little America was ideal for flying. The sky stretched clear and blue to all four horizons, except for a few puffs of cloud coming up over the horizon directly ahead. For the moment, they were nothing to be concerned about, and Balchen maintained a running check on his instruments as he flew the Ford Trimotor across the mighty Antarctic's frozen wastes.

Several hours slid by with the scenery below almost a constant stretch of unbroken ice and snow, and all three engines delivering at peak performance. Then Dr. Gould's rescue camp and weather station was sighted. Balchen took a moment to glance down at the tiny camp just barely silhouetted against the vast whiteness, and then he looked far ahead at the gleaming, icy terror that was the Queen Maud range.

To Balchen the mountains looked as though they rose right up through the roof of the sky— gigantic towers of ice and snow joining heaven and earth. He opened all three throttles wide and put the *Floyd Bennett* in a long climb that was to take the plane as high as she would go. The altimeter's needle moved slowly from six, to seven, and then to eight thousand feet, but the Queen Maud Mountains seemed to present a barrier of twice that height.

It was time to decide which route to try through the mountains—the Axel Heiberg Glacier or the Liv Glacier. The Heiberg was known to be some 10,500 feet high, and the Liv was believed to be a thousand feet lower. One was to the left of the big plane struggling for altitude and the other was to the right. Both looked formidable.

Balchen and Commander Byrd studied the two routes carefully, and it was finally decided to try to get through over the Liv Glacier. Balchen gently swung the big airplane toward it, still trying to get more altitude. The Liv Glacier certainly looked lower than the Heiberg, but the Ford was now flying at 8200 feet and the top of the Liv seemed at least five thousand feet higher.

The Ford gained another few hundred feet of altitude, but when it was still below nine thousand feet it ceased climbing. Balchen tried everything he could with the engines, but he could not make the aircraft gain another inch. The only hope was to jettison some of the weight, and it must be dumped in a hurry since the Liv was looming bigger and bigger.

Turning his head, he shouted at Harold June seated at the radio table.

"Quick! Dump some of the load. We can't get any more altitude with the weight aboard!"

June nodded and quickly reached for the fuel dump valve, but Balchen screamed at him, "No, not fuel! Throw out some of the food!"

The pilot of the aircraft had yelled the order, but the commander of the flight had ordered that the two bags of food be put aboard. June hesitated. Commander Byrd quickly seconded the order, however, and June opened the hatch in the floor and kicked out one of the 150-pound bags of food.

The aircraft started to climb again but only for another one hundred feet or so.

"Throw out the other bag of food!" Balchen yelled. "She's still too heavy to climb."

Harold June kicked out the second 150-pound bag of food. The Ford Trimotor started climbing again, its engines laboring mightily. The Liv Glacier was just beyond the nose now and Balchen had the feeling that the Ford was going to make it, or not make it, by a margin of no more than a couple of feet. As the aircraft approached the highest part of the glacier, however, a wild current of Antarctic air hit the underside of the plane's wings and sent it flying across the top-

most surface of the icy glacier with at least two hundred feet to spare.

They were through. Beyond was the polar plateau.

Midnight had long since come and gone, and it was the day after Thanksgiving. The Pole was only four hundred miles away and, putting the *Floyd Bennett* on the meridian course Commander Byrd ordered, Balchen flew onward toward their goal.

About three hours later Balchen made some calculations of his own and figured that they were only fourteen minutes flying time from the Pole. His calculations were absolutely correct. Just fourteen minutes later Commander Byrd gave Harold June the message to radio back to Little America:

We are over the South Pole.

For several minutes they circled above the spot that was the South Pole. The trap door in the floor was opened and Commander Byrd dropped an

American flag weighted with a stone from the grave of Floyd Bennett, who had piloted him to the North Pole, and two years later had died of pneumonia contracted while making a rescue flight to a crashed plane in the frozen wastes of the Hudson Bay area.

Eventually Commander Byrd gave the return course to Bernt Balchen, and after taking one last look at the gleaming whiteness of the Pole, he headed the Ford Trimotor back on the return flight.

This time when he approached the Liv Glacier in the Queen Maud Mountains he had no worries about the altitude. Much fuel had been used up on the last leg of the flight to the Pole and so the plane was considerably lighter. The plane was able to clear the glacier with ease and go sliding down to a landing on the spot where the reserve supply of gasoline was cached.

There the reserve fuel was poured into the Trimotor's tanks while Balchen kept the engines running. The rest of the flight to the camp was made without incident, and with very little talking by the four men aboard. They had conquered the South Pole by air but they were dead tired, and the constant thundering of the powerful Wright engines made conversation too much of a task.

Eighteen hours of actual flying time were recorded in the logbook when Balchen landed the Ford Trimotor smoothly on the firmly packed snow at the Little America camp. They were eighteen hours the four men, and the world, would never forget.

To Show the Way
Amelia Earhart

On the twenty-first of May, 1927, when word
was flashed to a waiting world that Charles Lindbergh had landed safely at Le Bourget Airdrome,
Paris, a young social worker at Denison House
in Boston, Massachusetts, was as excited and
thrilled as any of the countless millions who heard
the wonderful news. In addition, she was possessed with a burning desire someday to pilot an

airplane across the Atlantic ocean, herself.

Her name was Amelia Earhart, and she knew how to fly an airplane. She had taken lessons a few years before, had flown solo, and had eventually obtained her private pilot's license. As a matter of fact, she owned a small, light plane and had a total of some five hundred hours in her logbook. None of the hours, however, had been spent doing instrument flying in dirty weather, and none were spent working out navigation problems in strange skies. Nevertheless, her desire to pilot a plane across the Atlantic was great, and she was determined that some day she would.

One year and twenty-seven days later Amelia Earhart did cross the Atlantic by air, but not as the pilot of the aircraft, or even as a member of its working crew. She crossed as only a passenger, but that did earn her the distinction of being the first woman to cross the Atlantic by airplane.

A Mrs. Frederick Guest wanted to be the first woman passenger on a trans-Atlantic air crossing and had purchased a Fokker Trimotor. She engaged Wilmer Stultz to be its pilot and Lou Gordon to be its navigator. Mrs. Guest was the mother of two children, however, and when they learned of her intentions they prevailed upon her to abandon the idea. She still wanted a woman to make the air crossing in the three-engined Fokker she had named *Friendship*. Amelia Earhart was offered the chance, and she accepted eagerly.

At fifteen minutes after eleven o'clock on the morning of the seventeenth of June, 1928, Wilmer Stultz, Lou Gordon, and Amelia Earhart took off in the *Friendship* (fitted with pontoons in place of wheel landing gear) from Trepassey Harbor, Newfoundland, and headed eastward over the Atlantic Ocean.

Twenty-four hours and forty minutes later they reached the British Isles and landed safely at Burry Port in Wales.

Because she was a woman, and the first to cross the Atlantic in an airplane, the world

acclaimed her enthusiastically. She was feted in Europe and received by royalty, and when she returned to America aboard the *SS Roosevelt* she was given a grand ticker-tape parade up Broadway in New York and honored from coast to coast.

To a great many people, particularly aviation people, the wild acclaim for Amelia Earhart's air trip was way out of proportion to what she had actually achieved. She had been aboard the *Friendship* as a passenger and had contributed absolutely nothing toward making the flight the success it was. Stultz and Gordon had done all the work, so the wild acclaim for Amelia was not entirely justified.

That was the thought of a great many, and the one who thought it more strongly than anyone else was Amelia Earhart, herself.

To her it had been a great thrill and an exciting adventure, but her personal part in the flight was nothing, and in her own eyes she was just a phony heroine. Apart from being the first of her sex to cross the Atlantic by air, she had done nothing to merit the praise and acclaim she received in Europe and in the United States.

She said repeatedly, "All I did was lie on the floor like a sack of potatoes and admire the clouds we were flying over."

Feeling as she did, Amelia Earhart grimly resolved to prove she was more than a phony heroine, and that a woman pilot could take her place among men pilots.

Before she could prove it to the world, however, she first had to prove it to herself. She must first learn how to fly a plane on instruments, and how to navigate, and how to perform all the duties required of a pilot flying long distances over water and out of sight of land. When she had mastered all that, then she would make a solo flight across the Atlantic.

That a woman was going to fly in the *Friendship* as a passenger had been kept a closly guarded secret from the press until practically takeoff time. Amelia Earhart kept her preparations and plans for flying the Atlantic alone a very closely guarded secret. She purchased a Wright Whirlwind-powered Lockheed Vega monoplane, but, not wanting to give the press so much as an inkling of what she had in mind, she chartered the plane to Bernt Balchen, who was then making preparations with the polar explorer Lincoln Ellsworth for trailblazing flights into the Arctic. The members of the press knew what Balchen and

Ellsworth were planning, so they assumed that Amelia Earhart's Lockheed Vega would be used, and that she was merely aiding them in testing it for the proposed flights.

She had, of course, explained to Bernt Balchen what she wanted eventually to do and had asked his help in preparing herself and the Vega for a solo Atlantic crossing. Balchen quickly agreed to give her all the help he could. He believed she could acquire the knowledge and piloting experience necessary to make her capable of flying the Atlantic alone, and he was certain that he could put the Vega in perfect mechanical and aeronautical shape for such a flight.

Then began three years of intensive preparation for the solo flight. She put in a great many hours flying on instruments all over the country. She would pick a city some two or three hundred miles distant and take off and fly to it on instruments. When she hit her target she would turn around and return to her starting point on instruments. In the beginning she often missed target cities by a wide margin, but in time she was able to cut down the number of errors to almost nothing.

She studied navigation and the use of weather charts, and she spent many more hours in the air putting into practice all that she had learned. In addition, she practiced flying in all kinds of weather and got to know the Lockheed Vega and the Wright Whirlwind engine inside and out. She refused to leave anything to chance, and she did not attempt to complete her preparations in the shortest time possible. She was determined to be prepared in every respect when the time came to make the hazardous flight.

Her goal was to fly the Atlantic alone, but only the Atlantic. She had no intention of flying from New York to Paris as Lindbergh had done. As a matter of fact, it would be an extremely close thing to fly the Lockheed Vega from the United States to Europe, since its cruising range was only a little over three thousand miles.

She chose Harbor Grace in Newfoundland as her takeoff point, and on May 19, 1932, she was ready. The weather over the North Atlantic was reported to be favorable for the flight.

On the nineteenth Bernt Balchen and Eddie Gorski flew Amelia Earhart in the Lockheed Vega from Teterboro Airport in New Jersey to Harbor Grace in Newfoundland. A Pratt and Whitney Wasp engine had been installed in the aircraft to replace the Wright Whirlwind that had given her so many hours of faithful performance during her long preparation. The new Wasp performed perfectly during the flight northward.

The morning and afternoon of the following day, the twentieth, were spent giving the Lockheed a careful final check and studying the latest weather reports as they came in. The weather reports continued to show favorable conditions for the flight, and Amelia Earhart decided to go without further delay.

At thirteen minutes after seven o'clock that evening she said good-by to Bernt Balchen and Eddie Gorski, took off from the Harbor Grace runway, and headed out over the Atlantic.

Amelia Earhart was on her way to being the first woman to pilot an airplane across the Atlantic. And it was exactly five years to the day since Charles Lindbergh had blazed the air trail!

Holding the Lockheed Vega in a steady climb she went up through the sunset tinted heavens until she reached an altitude of twelve thousand feet. There she leveled off and put the aircraft on its first heading for the eastward flight.

Time and distance slid by as she maintained an alert check on her navigating and engine instruments. After a while the last of daylight faded and night closed down over her in the high air of the North Atlantic. A moon came out but it was blotted from sight by huge banks of clouds for long periods at a time. Now all she had learned about instrument flying and navigating stood by her,

and she flew onward toward the east, making her course changes at the correct times and holding the aircraft on its plotted route through the air.

Close to midnight she began running into weather that had not been mentioned in any of the reports she had received before taking off. Violent air currents started tossing the Vega all over the Atlantic sky, and it was all she could do to bring the aircraft back onto even keel and on course. A slashing rain, followed by thick fog, kept her eyes constantly on the instrument panel in front of her.

Presently ice began to form on the wings, adding that much more to the overall weight of the airplane. As if that were not trouble enough, a freezing temperature outside took its toll on the altimeter and put it completely out of commission, and ice plugged up the airspeed indicator so that it also became useless.

Her only sure guide was the Sperry Gyrocompass. It did not fail her, nor did the sturdy Pratt and Whitney Wasp engine in the nose. On occasion the Wasp did cough a little, but a careful fuel adjustment put it back to delivering maximum horsepower.

Finally, after a night that had seemed like an eternity, Amelia Earhart saw the first thread of dawn through the murky clouds far to the east. She had been in the air ten hours and had flown through just about every kind of weather. She had taken a terrific beating, both mentally and physically, but with the showing of that first dawn light the tension and the suspense began gradually to abate.

As the light increased she was able to see the clouds she was flying through and the cloud layers she flew between. Presently she was flying over holes in the clouds and she could see the gray Atlantic below. For the first time in hours she was able to get some idea of her approximate altitude.

She dropped down through one of the bigger

holes in the clouds into clear air and searched the rolling surface of the Atlantic for sight of a ship. She did not see any, but she remained low over the water to take advantage of the visibility which was fairly good.

By now all the ice on the wings had disappeared, but the altimeter and the airspeed indicator still did not function properly. That did not cause her half as much concern, however, as did the readings of the fuel gauges. They showed that she had used up three hundred of the 420 gallons put into the tanks at Harbor Grace.

Only 120 gallons left with which to reach land! There was no sign of it yet on the far horizon. Whether or not the violent weather she had encountered during the night had blown her off course she did not know, and there was no way she could check to find out. She thought she was now flying over shipping lanes, but she had not yet sighted any ships to confirm it. If she was north of her course the first land sighted should be Ireland, but if she was south it could very easily be France. The 120 gallons of fuel left in the tanks might not be enough to reach France.

Her only choice was to continue on the course she had plotted before the flight. An hour later she flew over the coast of Ireland. She did not know what part of Ireland it was, and because of low-level clouds and the non-functioning altimeter, she was reluctant to try to get under the clouds for a close inspection of the terrain below. She was, however, able to make out a set of railroad tracks, and as railroad tracks usually lead to a big city she decided to follow them.

Presently she sighted a fairly good-sized city, and holding her altitude she circled it several times, unable to ascertain the name of the city from her maps, and unable to sight any airport. But a few miles north of the city the low-hanging clouds ceased and the air was clear beyond.

Amelia Earhart banked the Vega away from the unidentified city and flew north into open sky.

Shortly afterward she spotted a field that looked big enough to land the Vega on, but she did not go down immediately and make a landing. She had crossed the Atlantic, but she certainly didn't want to terminate the flight with a careless crack-up landing.

She maneuvered the Lockheed Vega down to low level and made three or four passes over the field while she inspected it closely for half-hidden holes, or any other obstacles which might hinder a smooth landing. She saw none. And so, fourteen hours and fifty-six minutes after she had taken off from Harbor Grace, Newfoundland, she set the Vega down in a field by the village of Culmore, near the city of Londonderry, Ireland. A nonstop flight of 2,026 miles was completed.

By that flight Amelia Earhart proved to herself, and to the aeronautical world, that she was no phony heroine. This time when praise and honors were showered upon her there were none who said she had not earned them all.

Perhaps some other woman, having achieved her great goal, would have returned to pleasure flying and rested on her well-earned laurels for the rest of her life. But Amelia Earhart had no desire or intention of doing that.

The Atlantic flight was to be only a beginning. Now she wanted to make other long-distance flights, to show that the Atlantic flight was not just a stunt that she was lucky enough to get away with, and to prove for all time that the air belonged to women pilots as well as men.

That there was a place for women in the air was something she truly believed. She felt compelled to lead the way for her sex and prove her belief to be the truth.

And so, in her quiet and secretive way, she went about making plans for another long-distance flight. This one would also be over water. It would be from Honolulu in the Hawaiian Islands to San Francisco. It had been done several times by men pilots and Amelia Earhart decided it was now time for a woman to try it.

Amelia purchased a new Lockheed Vega, and after she had extensively test-flown it, and had installed extra fuel tanks and special instruments she would need for the long over-water flight, she had it crated and shipped to Honolulu. She obtained permission from the Navy to keep her plane at Wheeler Field. Her arrival in the Hawaiian Islands naturally created quite a lot of interest and speculation by the press. She was repeatedly asked if she was planning another long-distance flight, and each time she replied that she simply wanted to do a little flying about the Islands.

Though slightly misleading, the statement was nevertheless true, because she wanted to test-fly the new Lockheed Vega more extensively before taking off for San Francisco. For the next two weeks she did a lot of flying all over the Hawaiian Islands, and by the end of those two weeks she felt that both she and the airplane were ready for the long flight.

On the eleventh of January, 1935, reports on the weather between Honolulu and San Francisco were very favorable for air travel. At 4:45 that afternoon she took off in the Vega from Wheeler Field and headed out across the Pacific toward San Francisco.

For this flight the aircraft had been equipped with a radio. At no time was she out of touch with the rest of the world. She maintained her contact with certain ground stations and also with ships at sea, and was therefore able to keep an almost constant check on her position and course.

The flight to San Francisco required very little effort compared to her Atlantic crossing. It was just a matter of flying for fifteen hours and six minutes through clouds, fog, and rain, but on this trip she knew, every moment, exactly where she was. In time she spotted San Francisco's Golden Gate, and the Oakland Airport, where she landed.

Having accomplished the feat of flying non-

stop from Honolulu to San Francisco, the first
woman to do it, Amelia next made a seventeen-
hundred-mile flight from Burbank, California to
Mexico City, at the request of the Mexican president. While she was in Mexico City being en-
tertained and honored for her latest flight, she
decided to try a long-distance flight that had never
been attempted by a male pilot *or* a female pilot—
a nonstop flight from Mexico City to New York.

Two or three men pilots, whom she took into

her confidence in order to get their views on making such a flight, were very much opposed to her attempting it. For one thing, they pointed out, it was 2,125 miles from Mexico City to New York. For another, seven hundred of the air miles would be over the Gulf of Mexico. Also, Mexico City is eight thousand feet above sea level. In that thin air they did not think she could take the Vega off the ground with the load of fuel necessary for safety in the event that headwinds or storms cut down her ground speed and the flight took longer than she calculated.

Other reasons for not making the flight were presented but, after listening to them all, Amelia Earhart was still determined to try it.

With less fuel in the Vega's tanks than she had at first planned but, according to her calculations, enough to get her nonstop to New York, Amelia took off from Mexico City on the morning of the eighth of May, 1935. The flight was relatively uneventful. When she was over Washington, D.C., in the first darkness of night, and she reported her remaining fuel amount to those in radio contact with her at that point, she was advised to land at Washington. However, she decided to keep on toward Newark Airport, in New Jersey, as she had originally planned. Shortly after that she landed safely at Newark. She had spent exactly fourteen hours and eighteen minutes in the air.

For the next two years Amelia Earhart made no long-distance flights of record-breaking or history-making character, but during those two years she was again making plans and preparations for what she considered would be her greatest flight of all.

The world had been circled several times by aircraft with flight crews of two or more men. In 1933 Wiley Post had flown around the world solo in the *Winnie May*. All of those flights had been made along the shortest routes possible, however, and none of them involved anywhere near the distance that would be flown circling the earth at the equator.

It was Amelia Earhart's plan to circle the earth, by air, as near to the equator as possible.

The aircraft she purchased for the trip was a twin-engined Lockheed Electra monoplane. Because such a flight would require exceptionally skilled navigation, she selected Fred Noonan, a highly qualified expert on aerial navigation, to accompany her.

The first takeoff was from Miami, Florida, at five o'clock on the morning of June 1, 1937. From Miami, Amelia and Fred Noonan flew to Puerto Rico, and from there to Caripito in Venezuela. From that point they went down the South American coast to Paramaribo, in Surinam (Dutch Guiana), and to Fortaleza and Natal, in Brazil.

From Natal they crossed the South Atlantic to St. Louis, in French West Africa, and in four separate flights they crossed Africa and went on to India. They flew across India to Bangkok and then to Singapore. The next stop was Bandung, next Surabaja, and then Timor Island. From there they flew to Port Darwin, in Australia, and then on to Lae, in New Guinea.

When they landed at Lae they had flown 22,000 miles. The next stop was to be Howland Island, a tiny dot in seven thousand square miles of Pacific Ocean.

They never reached Howland Island.

On the second of July, at Lae, New Guinea, they took off for the long, over-water flight. For the first few hours a number of land stations and ships were able to make contact with the Lockheed Electra; after that there was nothing but silence from the aircraft, and all efforts to contact it by radio were to no avail.

Amelia Earhart, Fred Noonan, and the Lockheed Electra had simply vanished from the face of the earth. A vast sea and air search was organized, but no trace was ever found of them. Even today new clues appear and are investigated; new theories are put forth. But no one has ever learned what happened to Amelia Earhart, this remarkable woman who made the sky her own.

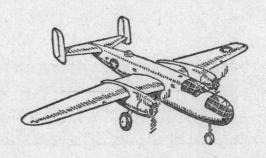

Top Secret
James H. Doolittle

In January of 1942, one month after Pearl Harbor, the United States forces in the Pacific were still reeling from the crippling sneak air attack by the Japanese. Here at home a shocked and angry nation was rallying to the colors and rolling up its sleeves for all-out war. And in Washington, D.C., top secret plans for a swift, surprise, retaliatory strike at the Japanese home islands were being put into operation.

The idea for the surprise strike is credited to Captain (later Admiral) Lowe, of the U.S. Navy, and it was to be a simultaneous air bombing of the Japanese cities of Tokyo, Yokohama, Osaka, Kobe, and Nagoya. The attack would be made from the deck of a Navy carrier after it had steamed under a cover of radio silence to a point within four hundred miles of the Japanese coast. The bombers would be launched so that they would arrive over their targets at night. When they had dropped their bombs they would fly on to predetermined airfields in China. Arriving there in the hours of daylight, they would refuel and continue on to Chungking to turn over their aircraft to the Chinese Air Force.

That was the plan and when it had been approved by Admiral King for the Navy, General Marshall for the Army, General Arnold for the Army Air Force, and President Roosevelt, a man was chosen to prepare and carry out the plan.

The man selected was James H. Doolittle, a former racing pilot, stunt pilot, and holder of many civilian and military flying records. At that time he was wearing the uniform of the U.S. Army Air Force, and on his shoulders was the insignia of a lieutenant colonel. The assignment given him was to select and prepare the aircraft to be used, and to select and train the crews. On accepting the assignment, Doolittle requested and received permission to lead the mission.

The aircraft that Doolittle selected to use was an Air Force B-25. He considered it perfect for the job as it had a short takeoff run, it was fast, and it could carry a fair-sized bomb load. The pilots and crews he selected were from the Seventh Bomber Group which was flying the B-25. Every man selected was a volunteer who would not learn the nature of the mission for which he was volunteering until shortly before takeoff.

As a Navy carrier could not be spared for deck takeoff training, that job would have to be done on marked-off runways on the ground; the place selected for this short-takeoff training and low-level bombing was Eglin Field near Pensacola, Florida. In addition to aircraft and aircraft crew preparations, there was the task of arranging with the Chinese Government for the use of certain airfields well back from the China coast and of arranging to have fuel supplies available at those fields when the bombing planes landed. There were a great number of things to be done, and all in utmost secrecy. Let word leak out to the Japanese and the entire mission would be doomed.

On the first of March, two months after the plan was conceived, Doolittle stood before the pilots and crews of twenty-four B-25 bombers gathered at Eglin Field. He looked them over and then gave it to them straight from the shoulder.

They had volunteered for an extremely dangerous job that would take them out of the country for two or three months. He couldn't tell them what kind of a job it was, or where it would be performed, or when. They would probably guess part of what it was all about as their training program progressed. What little they did guess they were to keep to themselves. The success of the job they would be trained to perform depended upon strict secrecy. They were not to talk about it to their wives or to any members of their families. They were to talk to *no one* about what they were doing.

Doolittle finished his short but very serious talk to the men by saying that if there were any of them who wished to drop out, now was the time to do it. No one dropped out.

The training began in earnest. Flags were spaced at certain intervals along the Eglin Field runway, and pilots and crews of the B-25's started practicing short takeoffs. When a pilot could get his plane off the ground by the time he reached the most distant flag, he was ready to aim for the next flag closer. Then the next and the next, until finally, with engines screaming and flaps down,

they were able to get their loaded aircraft off the runway by the time they reached the first flag. Night after night they practiced dropping dummy bombs, and a few times live ones, from low-level altitudes over certain designated targets in the area.

Eventually the pilots and crews attained a peak of performance they hadn't even dreamed was possible with a B-25. Of course they had guessed that the job they were training for must have something to do with a night bombing mission, but where and when was still a complete mystery to all of them.

Early on the morning of the twenty-fourth of March, the pilots and crews were routed out of bed and given orders to fly their planes to San Antonio, Texas. Whenever and wherever possible, they were to fly at hedgehopping height. They took off in the early dawn light, and when they landed at San Antonio orders were waiting for them to fuel up and fly north to March Field, and from there to McClelland Field in Sacramento, California.

Doolittle met them at McClelland Field, having flown his B-25 straight on through, and he issued orders that no one was to leave the field for any reason whatsoever. They were not to write letters, make telephone calls, or send any wires. They were to spend their time thoroughly checking their aircraft, and if they found even the slightest thing wrong they were to have the mechanics at the field take care of it immediately. At McClelland Field all radio equipment was removed from the aircraft, because, as Doolittle told them, they were not going to need it where they were going.

The pilots and crews got right to work, and two days later Doolittle ordered them to fly their planes to Alameda Field. When they landed, each pilot was asked by Doolittle what shape his aircraft was in. The pilots who said that there was something still not functioning properly were told to taxi their aircraft over to a hangar. Those who reported nothing wrong were instructed to taxi to a wharf on the far side of the field where the carrier *Hornet* was docked.

Eventually sixteen B-25's were hoisted aboard the *Hornet* and made fast to her huge flight deck.

The next morning the *Hornet,* with an escort of smaller ships, headed out into the broad expanse of the Pacific. The first day out, Doolittle assembled the pilots and crews and told them where they were going and what they were going to do. He gave each pilot a choice of target, and for himself he chose Tokyo. When targets were selected, the pilots and crews were given detailed maps showing the different airfields inside China where they would land to refuel and fly on to Chungking.

Day by day, as the *Hornet* steamed under strict radio silence toward Japanese waters, the pilots and crews worked on their aircraft, studied flight charts and maps, and attended lectures on Japanese and Chinese history, culture, customs, and their differences. The knowledge they gained might never be needed, but there was always the possibility of a crisis when this kind of information might save their lives. Doolittle was not leaving anything to chance. All measures possible were taken to insure the success of the daring venture, and the survival of those who were involved in it.

The pilots and crews who had chosen Tokyo as their target were ordered not to bomb the emperor's palace. Their targets were Japanese war plants and military installations, the destruction of which would hinder the Japanese war effort. The bombing of the palace would not benefit them in any way.

All pilots and crews were warned not to take along a single thing on their persons that could in any way, should they be shot down and captured, give the Japanese a hint that the U.S. Navy was connected with the operation. Not knowing where the bombers had come from would do almost as much to Japanese morale as would the exploding bombs.

In addition to the full gas tanks in each B-25, reserve fuel in five-gallon cans would be carried to be poured into the tanks during flight. The pilots and crews were warned not to throw any of the empty five-gallon cans overboard. They were to be kept aboard, because empty gasoline cans thrown into the water would mark a trail for Japanese pilots straight back to the *Hornet* and her escorting ships!

When the carrier force was still some distance from the point where the B-25's would be launched, Doolittle assembled the pilots and crews for the last time and gave the men a final chance to withdraw from the bombing mission if they wished to do so. Not a pilot or crew member withdrew.

The date set for the bombing attack was Sunday evening, the nineteenth of April. At that time the *Hornet* would be four hundred miles off the

Japanese coast. The sixteen B-25's would then take off from the flight deck and head for the various targets, reaching them under the cover of full night. And, as planned, they would drop their bombs and fly on to the airfields inside China.

However, at about half past seven on the morning of the eighteenth a Japanese patrol boat was sighted. During the night two enemy patrol boats had been avoided, but in hiding from the second patrol boat the carrier force had come upon the third one.

The patrol boat was quickly sunk by gunfire, but the question was, had it carried a radio? And if so, had the boat been sunk soon enough? In other words, did Japan now know that an American carrier force was within eight hundred miles of its shores?

If there had been no radio aboard the sunken Japanese patrol boat, then it was safe to proceed another four hundred miles to the point where it had been originally planned to launch the B-25's. But if there had been a radio on the patrol boat, it would be suicide to proceed with the original plan.

Land-based Japanese bombers, or possibly a Japanese carrier force that might be in those waters, could easily reach the *Hornet* and undoubtedly sink it. All the parking space on the *Hornet's* flight deck was taken up by the B-25 bombers. Her own planes were stored away with folded wings below decks. Should the enemy catch and attack the *Hornet* she would be virtually helpless—an ideal sitting-duck target for Japanese bombs and torpedoes.

The *Hornet* carrier force commander, Admiral Halsey, had no choice. He could not possibly risk an attack by the Japanese. The *Hornet* and her escorting ships had to turn tail and get out of those dangerous waters as swiftly as possible.

Doolittle did have a choice. He could lead his B-25 bombers off the flight deck and fly four hundred extra miles to the targets, reaching them in daylight instead of darkness, then continue on to China to reach the refueling airfields in darkness instead of daylight. Or, he could call off the entire bombing mission and go back with the *Hornet*.

It is easy to imagine the agony and torment Doolittle must have suffered in reaching his decision. Weeks and months of intensive preparation had been completed. Sixteen planes, pilots,

and crews in peak condition were ready to go tomorrow, as planned. But it could not be tomorrow; it had to be today. In fact, it had to be within
an hour or two. There would be four hundred extra miles of flying, when the original plan called
for a very slim margin of reserve fuel. It would be
daylight over the targets, instead of the dark of
night—darkness at the Chinese airfields instead
of daylight. All that, or forget the mission and return with the *Hornet*.

Doolittle decided to carry out the mission.

The pilots and crews of the bombers were sum-
moned to man their planes, and the aircraft were
trundled into position for takeoff on the flight
deck. All tanks had been filled and topped off,
and another five cans of fuel, five gallons each,
were put aboard each airplane. The additional
fuel would help, but no one could tell whether it
would be enough.

In short order, engines were barking into life
all over the flight deck. The *Hornet's* signalmen

took their posts, and flight deck crews stood by the chocks in front of the wheels. Inside each B-25 the pilot and crew made a last-minute check. The carrier *Hornet* had swung into the wind, pointed toward Tokyo, and was traveling at top speed.

At twenty-two minutes after eight o'clock, Doolittle, in the lead plane, braked hard, opened his engines wide, and signaled for the chocks to be yanked clear. He released the brakes and the B-25

lunged forward, picking up speed with every revolution of the propellers. The *Hornet* heaved in
the heavy, running seas, and at the right moment
Doolittle lifted the aircraft clear with room to
spare and practically stood it on its tail as he
climbed up into the overcast sky. At the top of the
climb he leveled off and cut around in a wide
circle to come roaring over the *Hornet* as she
cleaved the water toward Japan.

Had it been possible to carry out the original
plan, Doolittle would have circled about until
all sixteen B-25's were off, but with his fuel the
most precious thing in the world to him at the
moment, he could not waste any of it waiting to
see if everybody got off the *Hornet's* flight deck.
It so happened that all the bombers did get off
safely, but by then Doolittle was out of sight of the
carrier on his way toward Tokyo.

An hour or so after leaving the carrier, Doolittle flew out of the fairly dirty weather and into
sunshine. Holding the bomber at practically wave-

top level, to hide from Japanese radar, he maintained a constant check on his course and instrument readings. At noon the coastline of Japan was sighted, and minutes later Doolittle's B-25 roared over the coast and went streaking straight for Tokyo.

As his bomber was the first off the *Hornet's* deck it was the first over Tokyo, and the surprise it created was paralyzing in its effect. He and his crew members saw people standing frozen in their tracks, gaping upward, and then racing for cover long after the B-25 had flashed by.

The entire load of bombs was dropped for bull's-eye hits on the predetermined targets, but Doolittle and his crew bitterly regretted that they couldn't have carried more bombs. They flew over many other inviting targets, but by then their bomb racks were empty.

In about thirty seconds all of Tokyo was behind them, and so were some Japanese fighter planes that had taken off but were not fast enough to catch up with the B-25. After a while the whole of Honshu, the biggest of the Japanese Islands, was behind them, and the B-25 was roaring out over the Sea of Japan toward Korea. In time it flew across Korea and then across the Yellow Sea toward the coast of China.

Over the Yellow Sea the airplane ran into stormy weather and, as it bored through head winds that cut down its ground speed, the fuel supply in the tanks grew lighter. All the reserve fuel had now been poured into the tanks, but with the aircraft bucking heavy winds the chances of the fuel supply lasting seemed remote indeed.

The weather grew even worse as they neared the China coast. Huge black storm clouds blocked it off, and rather than risk the violent turbulence he was sure must be inside those gigantic clouds, Doolittle sacrificed precious fuel to climb up above them and set a course for Choo Chow Lishui where he was supposed to land and refuel for Chungking. Again and again he checked time and fuel, and with each check the chance of even reaching the Choo Chow Lishui area seemed poorer.

At about ten o'clock that night, as the B-25 winged onward through the black China sky, Doolittle knew for certain that they were not going to make Choo Chow Lishui. They were not even near it, and the last bit of fuel in the plane's tanks was being swiftly sucked into the roaring engines. A few minutes of flying time were all they had left.

Doolittle ordered his crew to bail out and, as he held the B-25 steady, one by one the crew members parachuted into the darkness below. When the last crew member had jumped into the China night, and the engines had started to sputter for want of fuel, Doolittle bailed out of the aircraft, himself.

He landed, after a long descent through clouds and rain, in a rice paddy. He waded out of it to firm ground, and since he had no idea where he was, he decided it would be best to sit out the darkness.

When dawn came he picked a direction at random and started walking. Whether he was in a part of China already occupied by Japanese forces, he did not know. He kept on the alert for Japanese soldiers, and when he finally did come upon a little village he studied it carefully for some time before entering. Fortunately, there were no Japanese in the village, or very near at hand. The

brave Chinese of the village took him in and hid him whenever enemy patrols did pass through. And, eventually, they helped him to succeed in reaching Chungking.

Not a single B-25 that took off from the flight deck of the *Hornet* was able to reach its originally planned landing field. One pilot and crew, after dropping their bombs, headed for Siberia and were able to land safely near Vladivostok, where they were interned. Two other aircraft ran out of fuel just as they reached the China coast and crashed on the landing attempt. All the other pilots and crews bailed out over China in the dark of night.

Of the eighty who took part in the bombing raid, only three crew members lost their lives during the flight. Two were drowned when their aircraft landed in the water on the coast of China and one was killed when he bailed out. Eight others were taken prisoner by the Japanese in

China. Three of these were executed, and one died of malnutrition. And so, of the eighty brave men, only seven were lost, directly or indirectly, as a result of the Tokyo bombing raid.

The surviving pilots were decorated on their return to the United States, and Jimmy Doolittle was awarded the Congressional Medal of Honor.

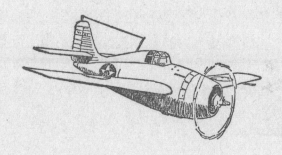

A Long Trip Home
Joseph Foss

Not long after the attack on Pearl Harbor, Japanese army, navy, and air forces occupied the Solomon Islands in the South Pacific. The islands were fortified against attack, and preparations were begun for an assault on Australia.

In the first part of August, 1942, a force of U.S. Marines, supported by Navy ships and converted carrier-based aircraft, waged an attack on one of the Solomon Islands, called Guadalcanal. After one of the bloodiest battles in the entire Pacific war, the Marines succeeded in getting a foothold on Guadalcanal and captured an airfield the Japanese had begun.

The Marines completed the building of the field, under constant savage attack by Japanese bombers and fighting planes, and Japanese troops hidden in the jungle that bordered almost one half of the airfield's perimeter. From the seventh of August, the first day of the attack, until the twenty-first, the Marines were completely without land-based air cover. Finally, on the twenty-first, Henderson Field was completed and American fighter planes were flown in from converted carriers standing far offshore.

Not many fighter planes were flown into Henderson Field at the start, for the simple reason that there were not many fighter planes available right then. The number, however, did increase steadily, and by September the Marine ground forces, fighting savagely to increase their foot-hold on Guadalcanal, were getting strong air cover from Henderson Field-based aircraft.

All that time the Japanese army, navy, and air forces mounted attack after attack in a furious attempt to destroy Henderson Field and drive the Marines back into the sea. The Japanese ground forces launched countless attacks from the jungle bordering the airfield and the entire area occupied by Marine troops. Japanese ships offshore hurled in thousands of big shells, and ten or a dozen times a day Japanese planes bombed and strafed Ameri-can-held positions.

On the seventh of October, a group of Grum-man Wildcat fighter planes arrived at Henderson Field after flying off an American carrier far at sea. The group was led by a former farm boy from South Dakota, Joe Foss.

At that time Joe Foss was a captain. He and his squadron had come to Henderson Field to bolster the air cover that was still far from adequate for

the tremendous task it faced. And, although nobody knew it at the time, Joe Foss had also come
to Henderson Field to establish a record which
has never been matched in the history of aerial
warfare. A total of twenty-six aircraft shot down
in only sixty-three days of aerial combat!

Joe Foss shot down his first Japanese aircraft
on the thirteenth of October, and he shot down his
last three in a single day, January 15, 1943. His
top bag for one day was accomplished on the
twenty-fifth of October, when he shot down five
Japanese Zeros.

There were good days and bad days for Joe
Foss over Guadalcanal, just as there were for all
the other pilots based at Henderson. But one
particular day was both good and bad for Foss—
November 7, 1942.

During the morning of the seventh there was
relatively little activity by the Japanese land, sea,
and air forces. The Japanese ships usually bom-
barded the field at night; there was no bombard-

ment at all during that morning. There was nothing but light, intermittent fire by the enemy forces entrenched in the jungle bordering the field. Japanese aircraft did not come over at all.

The pilots at Henderson Field sat around, doing whatever they wished, but ready to race to their waiting aircraft the instant an alert was sounded. Nothing happened until afternoon, and then it was not an attack alert that ended their hours of rest. It was a report that some five or six small Japanese navy vessels had been sighted a hundred miles north of Guadalcanal. The stand-by flights at Henderson Field were ordered to take off and engage the sighted ships.

Joe Foss's flight was one of the units ordered to the attack on the Japanese vessels, and he immediately led his flight into the air and headed north. Within an hour he sighted the six small ships steaming south toward Guadalcanal. He was about to radio the order to his flight to go down and attack when he saw a flight of six

Japanese Zeros a little ahead of and below him.

He also saw something else that stopped him from radioing the order to dive on the vessels and attack with heavy machine-gun fire. It was another of the Grumman Wildcat flights from Henderson Field, and it was flying along just ahead of and below the Zeros, obviously unaware that the enemy planes were above and behind.

As a matter of fact, just as Foss sighted the Zeros and the Grummans, the Japanese pilots opened fire on the unsuspecting Wildcat pilots.

"Let's go get 'em!" Foss shouted over his radio.

As one, the seven pilots of Foss's flight dropped their noses and went streaking down across the sky to pick their Zero and blaze away with all five guns each Grumman carried. Foss was the first to get one of the Zeros. A bull's-eye burst of machine-gun fire blew it apart in the air and sent it tumbling seaward in pieces.

No sooner had Foss nailed his man than he went cutting around to hunt out another victim.

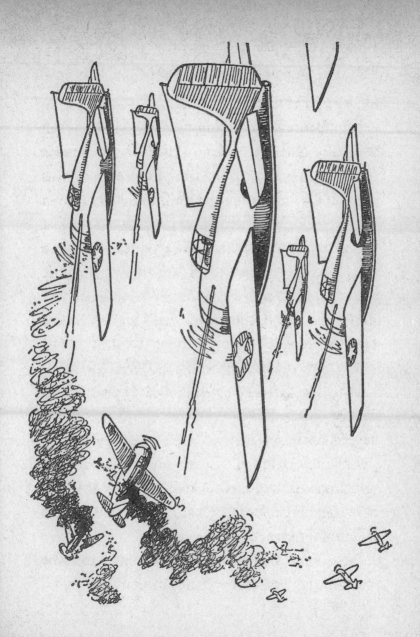

But there were no other Japanese Zeros left in the air. Every one of the six Japanese planes had been shot out of the air in a matter of seconds. In fact, before the other flight of Grummans had been able to wheel around and up to join in the battle, the Zeros had been destroyed.

Instead of starting the attack on the Japanese vessels as two separate flights, the Grumman pilots formed a single unit of fourteen aircraft, for more concentrated firepower, and got ready for the long dive.

Just as Foss was about to go into his dive, however, he suddenly caught sight of the under-side of a Japanese plane half-hidden in some clouds above him. It could be a lagging member of the Zero flight just destroyed, its pilot back up in the clouds for safety reasons, but it could also be a spotting plane. If the latter, it would wait for the Marine planes to go down for the attack, then radio a large force of Japanese planes hiding above the clouds. They would dive on the Grummans with the advantages of height and rear-attack position in their favor.

Calling over the radio to his pilots to continue their diving attack, Joe Foss broke away and headed around and up toward the clouds. As he climbed he saw that the Japanese plane was a two-seater scout type, and he was about to open fire when he realized that his closing speed was so great he had to sheer off or he would fly right into the Japanese plane.

As it was, he just barely missed clipping it with a wing. A quick burst from the Japanese observer's guns put holes in his plane's wing as he went streaking by. The Japanese pilot tried desperately to fly deep into the clouds and out of sight, but before he could succeed Foss had whipped around and was coming in on him, guns blazing. The observation plane flipped over onto one wing and dropped into a slow spiral that continued all the way down to the water far below.

As soon as the Japanese observation plane hit

the water, Foss started to climb up through the clouds to see if there was a force of enemy planes hiding above. Suddenly, a second Japanese observation plane came sliding down out of the cloud bank. Foss hardly had to maneuver his Grumman into firing position. The other plane was practically flying broadside. One short, close-range burst of fifty-caliber machine-gun bullets and the Japanese plane became a ball of fire falling toward the sea.

Foss didn't wait to watch it hit the water. No sooner was it hurtling down than he sent his Grumman up through the clouds and out on top of them. After taking a good look about the sky, and sighting no other Japanese plane, he went diving back to join in the attack on the Japanese surface ships.

When he came out of the clouds he could see three or four columns of smoke coming up from the water below, but he could not sight a single one of the thirteen Wildcats that had made the attack. That there were no Grummans below was obvious. The attack had been made, the targets either destroyed or hopelessly crippled, and the attacking planes had flown back to Henderson Field.

Foss was pleased that the attack had been a success, but he was not very pleased with the position in which he now found himself. One of the things he had learned in short order, upon arriving at Henderson Field for combat duty, was that a straggler or lone pilot flying around on his own was just begging for trouble from Japanese aircraft. Japanese pilots were hawks for lone planes, and more than one Marine pilot had found that out and paid for it with his life.

Foss set a course for Henderson Field, and he kept as close as he could to clouds so he could duck into them and lose himself, should a flight of Japanese planes suddenly appear and come after him. As he flew along he scanned the sky for enemy planes, and also for American planes he could join for the flight back to Henderson. Twice he did see a small group of American planes, but they were too far away for him to catch and join them, and he soon lost them in rain squalls sweeping across the sea.

After a while he ran into the squalls, but rain squalls were an everyday experience for pilots flying out of Henderson, so they gave him no concern. When he sighted an especially large one, however, he decided to skirt it instead of flying straight through it. A good-sized rain squall can have some pretty violent air currents, and since his Wildcat had been hit by Japanese bullets during that last fight it would be foolish to risk possible structural failure by flying straight through the bad weather.

According to his reckoning he would find, just beyond the squall, two fair-sized islands in the rough shape of arrows pointing straight toward Guadalcanal. He had only to line up his Wildcat when he was over them and he would be dead on course. But, when he had circled the squall, the two arrow-shaped islands were not there. He saw some islands, but they were not familiar ones.

He was lost.

Foss realized he had failed to keep a close enough check on his compass after leaving the area of the burning Japanese ships. Now he had no idea how far he was from Henderson Field, or what compass course he must fly to reach it. And, to make matters even worse, at just about that moment the Grumman's engine started to cough and sputter. He tried everything he could to get the engine operating full power, but his efforts failed. A few moments later it gave one last gasp and quit cold.

Putting the Grumman into a shallow glide and holding it there, Foss stared at the island closest to him. It was fair-sized but appeared to be covered with dense jungle growth from one end to the other. There were no level strips of beach where an airplane could land. Even if there had been, it wouldn't have raised his spirits any, for he knew the Grumman didn't have the height to glide down and land on a beach. As a matter of fact, he knew he would be lucky if he came down in the water no more than a mile from shore.

The heavily armored Wildcat dropped like a rock when it finally lost flying speed. It hit the water hard and made one long skipping bounce, hit once more, floated for two or three seconds, and then sank nose first.

Almost before Foss could start getting out of the cockpit, he and the plane were several feet underwater. He had to yank himself loose from the seat straps before the buoyancy of the parachute he still wore shot him up to the surface. When he did reach the surface he was forced to float face down in the water because of the buoyancy of the parachute pack on his back. Striving to hold his breath, but nevertheless gulping in quite a bit of salt water, he finally managed to get out of the parachute harness. When he did, his "Mae West" held him upright in the water.

After he got his breath he started swimming toward the island, but he could make no headway at all. At last he gave up trying to swim and resigned himself to drifting with the current away from the island.

An hour later, when darkness settled, he was still drifting, one hand clutching the strap of his floating parachute pack. During that hour of light he had searched the sky for sight of Marine planes out searching for him, but he had seen none. He had stared, too, at the island, fearful that it might be occupied by Japanese who had seen his plane crash in the water, hoping it was occupied only by natives, and that they would come out in a boat and rescue him. He saw no signs of human life at all on the island.

Darkness came. Foss fought off despair. What would the fellows at Henderson Field be doing now? he wondered. Would a search for him be flown? What would his wife, June, think when she received word he was missing in action? And just how long could a life jacket keep a man afloat? Would the current change and carry him back toward the island? Was there anything on the island to keep a man alive, and for how long?

Joe Foss had many thoughts, and one great fear—sharks. He knew that the waters off the Solomon Islands were infested with sharks, but during that hour of daylight he had not seen the dreaded shark's fin slicing through the water.

After darkness settled down, however, there were two or three times when he was sure he saw the dim outline of a fin slowly circling about him. He held his breath and didn't move a muscle for minutes on end.

He had been in the water over two hours when he heard the unmistakable chunking sound of canoe paddles. His first thought was that Japanese forces did occupy the island and that they were now out hunting for him. By the sounds he could tell there was more than one canoe, and as they drew closer he went rigid again so as not to reveal his presence. Someone was holding up a lantern in the canoe nearest to him, and he instinctively bent his head in order to present as little of his face as he could to the lantern's light.

Presently, one of the canoes slid by him not ten feet away. When it was no more than its own length past him, he heard a voice call out from the other outrigger canoe.

"Come look over here! The current would drift

him more in this direction!"

On hearing English spoken Joe Foss let the clamped air out of his lungs in a loud yell. A few moments later the outrigger had swung around and its occupants pulled him and his parachute pack aboard.

The men in the two canoes were from a mission on the island, the membership of which was composed of a number of different nationalities. They had seen him crash and get out of the sinking plane and had come searching for him as soon as they could. They assured him that there were no Japanese forces on the island. No Japanese had ever come near it.

When they had taken him ashore they gave him dry clothes, food to eat, and assigned him the best bed in the mission. But they knew very little about the war and how it was progressing, so Joe Foss had to answer a great many questions that night before they would let him go to sleep.

The next day a Grumman Wildcat flew over the island and came back to circle it a couple of times before flying off again. Its pilot had seen the parachute envelope spread out in the sun to dry. Later that day a Navy flying boat landed as close to the shore as its pilot dared. Foss was paddled out to it in one of the outriggers and an hour later he was back at Henderson Field.

As soon as another Grumman Wildcat could be fitted up for him, Joe Foss was flying more combat patrols and shooting down more Japanese planes. He bagged four to make his total twenty-three, and then an attack of malaria put him out of the war for six weeks. He returned to Henderson Field in early January of 1943, and on the thirteenth, his last day of combat flying, he shot down three enemy planes to make his grand total twenty-six.

That number made him the top air ace of the Pacific War at that time. It equaled the number of enemy aircraft that Captain Eddie Rickenbacker had shot down in World War I.

After destroying twenty-six Japanese planes in the air, Joe Foss was ordered to Washington, D.C., for two reasons. One was to take up his new duties of giving speeches for war bonds and incentive talks to factory workers. The other was to be decorated by President Roosevelt with the Congressional Medal of Honor.

Whitman
CLASSICS

Five Little Peppers Midway

Freckles

Wild Animals I Have Known

Rebecca of Sunnybrook Farm

Alice in Wonderland

Mrs. Wiggs of the Cabbage Patch

Fifty Famous Fairy Tales

Rose in Bloom

Eight Cousins

Little Women

Little Men

Five Little Peppers and How They Grew

Robinson Crusoe

Treasure Island

Heidi

The Call of the Wild

Tom Sawyer

Huckleberry Finn

Black Beauty

Here are some of the best-loved stories of all time. Delightful . . . intriguing . . . never-to-be-forgotten tales that you will read again and again. Start your own home library of WHITMAN CLASSICS so that you'll always have exciting books at your finger tips.

Whitman

REG. U.S. PAT. OFF.

ADVENTURE and MYSTERY Books

Mystery Stories for GIRLS and BOYS

TRIXIE BELDEN

The Secret of the Mansion
The Mysterious Visitor
The Red Trailer Mystery
The Gatehouse Mystery
The Mystery Off Glen Road
The Mystery in Arizona
The Happy Valley Mystery
The Marshland Mystery
The Black Jacket Mystery
The Mysterious Code

DONNA PARKER

In Hollywood
At Cherrydale
Special Agent
On Her Own
A Spring to Remember
Mystery at Arawak

TROY NESBIT SERIES

The Forest Fire Mystery

From Walt Disney's Wonderful Movies...

Hans Brinker
Toby Tyler

Exciting Stories for Young Readers...

THE BOBBSEY TWINS

In the Country
Merry Days Indoors and Out
At the Seashore

New Stories About Your Television Favorites...

The Rebel

The Real McCoys
Danger at the Ranch

Dr. Kildare
Assigned to Trouble

Janet Lennon
Adventure at Two Rivers
Camp Calamity

Walt Disney's Annette
The Desert Inn Mystery
Sierra Summer
The Mystery at
Moonstone Bay

The Lennon Sisters
Secret of Holiday Island

Leave It to Beaver

Ripcord